D1070480

# THE MYTH OF SIMPLICITY

PRENTICE-HALL INTERNATIONAL, INC., *London*
PRENTICE-HALL OF AUSTRALIA, PTY., LTD., *Sydney*
PRENTICE-HALL OF CANADA, LTD., *Toronto*
PRENTICE-HALL FRANCE, S.A.R.L., *Paris*
PRENTICE-HALL OF JAPAN, INC., *Tokyo*
PRENTICE-HALL DE MEXICO, S.A., *Mexico City*

MARIO BUNGE

# THE MYTH OF SIMPLICITY

## Problems of Scientific Philosophy

PRENTICE-HALL, INC.
*Englewood Cliffs, N.J.*
1963

*OTHER RECENT WORKS BY THE SAME AUTHOR*

*Causality: The Place of the Causal Principle in Modern Science*
New York: Meridian Books, Inc., 1963, 2nd ed.

*Causalidad* [Translation of the foregoing]
Buenos Aires: Editorial Universitaria de Buenos Aires, 1961.

*Metascientific Queries*
Springfield, Ill.: Charles C. Thomas, 1959.

*Cinemática del electrón relativista*
Tucumán: Universidad Nacional de Tucumán, 1960.

*Antología semántica* (editor)
Buenos Aires: Nueva Visión, 1960.

*Etica y ciencia*
Buenos Aires: Siglo Veinte, 1960.

*La ciencia*
Buenos Aires: Siglo Veinte, 1960.

*Intuition and Science*
Englewood Cliffs, N.J.: Prentice-Hall, Inc., 1962.

*The Critical Approach: Essays in Honor of Karl Popper* (editor)
New York: The Free Press of Glencoe, Inc., 1963.



Library of Congress Catalog Card No. 63-8287

PRINTED IN THE UNITED STATES OF AMERICA

60913—C

# Preface

The aims of this book are two. First, to contribute to the elucidation of some key concepts of both philosophy and science, such as those of conceptual analysis, analyticity, truth, law, level, and simplicity. Second, to show the complexity, i.e., the richness, of those very concepts, thereby exploding the myth that simplicity is always either a fact or a desideratum of research. To the extent to which the book succeeds in attaining both goals it should discourage the concoction of naïve, oversimplified pictures of knowledge.

The method employed is a kind of philosophic procedure that may be called metascientific elucidation. This kind of clarification may be analytic or synthetic: it may consist either in the analysis or reduction of conceptual entities (concepts, propositions, theories), or in the construction of such entities. In either case, whether in the phase of analysis or in the phase of synthesis, I call this work metascientific if the objects of elucidation are relevant to science and if the task is performed in a way congenial to science and with the help of some of the tools of contemporary scientific philosophy, such as formal logic, semantics, and theory formalization.

To the extent to which the ideas dealt with in this book are relevant to science and therefore of interest to both scientists and philosophers of science, and to the extent to which the analyses and syntheses proposed do take advantage of the tools of scientific philosophy, this is a work on metascientific elucidation. But it is not a purely technical, neutral book. Unlike most scientific discourse, philosophizing, even if constructive, is more or less polemical: an opponent or, rather, a rival theory, method, or aim is always in sight or in the background of every philosophic activity—save in pure logic.

In the present case, the opponents are friends in the large and complex camp of illuministic philosophy, by which I understand the philosophy that at least wishes to make friends with logic and science and rejects obscurantism. I shall call those friends whom I am criticizing philosophic dadaists and cubists. By philosophic Dadaism I mean the seraphic belief in simple ultimates, in the necessity of drastically reducing the number of basic concepts, in the existence of entirely safe entities (e.g., sense data), and in the possibility of depicting every theory about theories with a few simple strokes. Philosophic Cubism, very close to Dada, operates in the construction of rigorous but utterly artificial "languages" or theories, remote from living science and therefore of little interest in the understanding of knowledge. Both philosophic dadaists and philosophic cubists are stern believers in the Myth of Simplicity.

Elegant and logically clean as they are, philosophic Dadaism and Cubism are neither the right answer to the hollow rhetoric of philosophic Baroque nor the right reaction against the uneventfulness of philosophic Classicism. Not a trivialization of problems and an impoverishment of ideas, but a deepening and renewal of both are required to counteract Baroque and Classicism. In philosophy, even more than in art, an experimental and critical realism is the sound and fruitful view. The desirable complexity that accompanies both depth and span can then be opposed to the redundancies of Baroque, and the critical alertness that secures progress can then be proposed in place of the rigidity of Classicism. The oversimplification of Dadaism and the artificiality of Cubism can thereby be avoided.

All oversimplification should be avoided in science and in philosophy, except as a temporary methodological device enabling us to start work or to apply its results. Simplicity, a practical and aesthetic desideratum, becomes dangerous if promoted to the rank of universal norm, particularly in matters of knowledge. For here it can consecrate ignorance and, what is worse, the refusal to learn—i.e., dogmatism. In fact, simplicism is at the root of school philosophy, with its characteristic onesidedness. The recipe for founding a school of philosophy is, indeed, this: "Take a half-truth (and, if need be, even a full truth) and proclaim it as the sole truth. Paradigms: from the fact that knowing requires experiencing, conclude that experience is the alpha and the omega of knowledge; from the fact that some processes are in fact dialectical, jump to the conclusion that all of them are; base conventionalism on the fact that action and language embody conventions." The critique of simplicism is consequently an integral part of the criticism of school philosophies, those remnants of prescientific philosophy that are dying partly because they refuse to recognize the increasing complexity of the human adventure.

Let me conclude with three warnings. First, this is not a textbook but a problem book, which reports on what has been going on in the corner of the philosophy workshop where controversial questions are asked and worked out. Second, this book is not addressed to a narrow sector of specialists but to students coming from all walks of academic life, with a critical frame of mind and an interest in key ideas related to the kernel of contemporary intellectual culture: namely, science. Although the technical passages in the book constitute only a small part of it, it is not claimed that the book is simple. How could this claim be made if one of its aims is to expose the inadequacy of simplicism? The third warning is that I regard everything that is said herein as corrigible, precisely because I wish philosophizing were always done in a scientific mood.

*Mario Bunge*

# Acknowledgments

Most of the chapters in this book have been delivered in lecture form at a dozen North American universities, where I had the privilege of hearing expert criticism. I am grateful for the criticisms made on various points by several anonymous students and referees, and by Professors C. E. Alchourrón (Buenos Aires), M. Beardsley (Swarthmore), P. Bernays (Zürich), R. Cartwright and H. N. Castañeda (Wayne), P. Caws (Kansas), D. Finkelstein (Yeshiva), N. Goodman, E. Grosswald, H. Hiż, R. D. Luce, and R. McNaughton (Pennsylvania), K. R. Popper (London), A. Raggio (Córdoba), J. G. Roederer (Buenos Aires), and R. Schiller (Stevens). I have also profited from short discussions with the late P. W. Bridgman (Harvard) and Professors P. Frank (Harvard), M. A. Melvin (Florida), and D. C. Williams (Harvard). But above all I thank the most uncompromising, profound, and constructive of my critics: my wife Marta.

The book contains long excerpts from articles published in various journals. An earlier version of Chapter 2 appeared in *Mind,* LXX, 239 (1961), and of Chapter 3 in *Review of Metaphysics,* **13,** 396 (1960). The substance of Chapters 4 and 5 was presented to the Stanford International Congress for Logic, Methodology and Philosophy of Science (1960) and published in the *Journal of Philosophy,* LIX, 113 (1962). Parts of Chapter 7 have appeared in *Philosophy of Science,* **28,** 120 (1961); an earlier version of Chapter 9 in the same review, **27,** 262 (1960), and parts of Chapter 10 again in the same journal, **28,** 260 (1961) and in *Scientia,* **55,** 1 (1961). Chapter 11 appeared in a slightly different form in the *American Scientist,* **49,** 432 (1961) and Chapter 12, also with some changes, in the *American Journal of Physics,* **29,** 518 (1961). I am most grateful to the editors of these journals for their kind permission to use these articles as source materials.

# Table of Contents

## II. SIMPLICITY AND TRUTH

# THE MYTH OF SIMPLICITY

# I
# ANALYSIS

# 1

# Metascientific Elucidation

Thinking begins with forming, associating and elaborating ideas; it culminates with synthesizing them into bodies of grounded and testable opinion. But *critical* thinking—the thinking peculiar to science, technology, rational philosophy, and rational decision making—begins when we start to analyze both initial ideas and final (but still corrigible) syntheses. Science and, to a lesser degree, technology are eminently testable and, by the same token, critical or analytic. And so is every philosophy which purports to be rational, that is, arguable—and a fortiori every philosophy which claims the right to be called scientific, that is, testable and congenial with science.

Nonanalytic outlooks and philosophies, such as intuitionism, are of course irrationalistic; in extreme cases, like existentialism, they are not only obscurantist but even perverse.[1] Analysis is the only rational deterrent to word magic, the only means for dissolving the mist of high-sounding but thoughtless declamations and slogans; besides, it is a powerful thawer of dogma. Analytic alertness is, therefore, more than a disposition to intellectual gymnastics and a vaccine against wordiness: analysis is indispensable for the survival of culture in an age in which every single individual is subjected to the pressure, brutal or subtle, of overt and covert persuaders aiming at preventing him from thinking critically and rationally.

The effect of analysis is, in fact, opposite to that of propaganda: it is dissuasive rather than persuasive, it allows assent only after successful genuine tests, and even then the assent it permits is provisional, that is, susceptible to ultimate revision. Assenters may make good slaves, soldiers, and monks, but only rational dissenters and critical constructors may plan, build, and preserve a free and progressive society.

## 1. *Analytic Philosophy*

Enlightened philosophers nowadays like to call themselves analytic. But the phrase 'analytic philosophy' is a redundancy: no theory of ideas—and philosophy is precisely a set of theories of ideas—can afford to be nonanalytic unless it is prepared to be nonsensical. It is only out of politeness towards professors captured by irrationalistic pseudophilosophies that we retain the qualifier 'analytic' when 'philosophy' should suffice. Likewise, it is unnecessary to speak of 'open science': occult or secret "science" is no science at all.

Moreover, the name *analytic philosophy* becomes misleading if applied exclusively to the kind of philosophizing restricted to an examination of ordinary language and some

[1] See, e.g., M. Bunge, *Intuition and Science* (Englewood Cliffs, N. J.: Prentice-Hall, Inc., 1962), Chapters 1 and 4.

classical problems of philosophy.[2] The unconditional surrender to common sense—that precursor of critical thinking—renders it a half-way analysis, even though in some cases it is performed with remarkable ingenuity. 'Semianalytic philosophy' would be a more adequate name. And for that considerable part of the so-called linguistic philosophy which deals chiefly with the current usage of current terms and imposes the boundary condition of never clashing with ordinary knowledge, 'prescientific linguistic semianalysis' would be an even better denomination. This harsh treatment of commonsensical analysis of daily life and daily English parlance does not imply its rejection. Linguistic philosophy is a good preamble to philosophy and an excellent literary exercise: it has a right to life, but it has no right to be called philosophy—if only because it is not in love with knowledge.

Furthermore, an excessive emphasis upon the term 'analytic' may give the impression that philosophy is nothing but analysis. A philosopher may restrict himself to analysis; but philosophy, as a rational corpus rather than as an activity, is a set of theories. An analytic bent is the very least that can be expected from a philosopher, just as a searching (undogmatic) attitude is to be expected from the scientist and a nonconformist attitude from the good citizen. But critical examination alone, though preferable to the uncritical repetition of some frozen body of beliefs, does not quench our thirst for knowledge. Criticism is no substitute for work, whether it be in everyday life, in science, or in philosophy.

Analysis is a prerequisite of intellectual creation but not its substitute, just as hygiene, accounting and public debates are

[2] The so-called Oxford philosophy is best represented by the journals *Mind* and *Proceedings of the Aristotelian Society,* and by G. Ryle's *The Concept of Mind* (London: Hutchinson, 1949) and L. Wittgenstein's *Philosophical Investigations* (New York: The Macmillan Co., 1953). Good general expositions will be found in M. Weitz, "Oxford Philosophy," *Journal of Philosophy,* 62 (1953), 187-233 and J. O. Urmson, *Philosophical Analysis* (Oxford: Clarendon Press, 1956).

necessary for civilized life but do not constitute the heart of life. What we expect from philosophy, as from science, is, above all, theories: theories about the world and theories about our knowledge of the world. Scientific and philosophic activities which do not yield theories may be necessary but are insufficient.

## 2. *Kinds of Analysis*

Scientific analysis can be of things and facts (events and processes) as well as of ideas. Philosophic analysis, on the other hand, bears only on concepts, propositions, and theories, which in turn may refer to further conceptual entities or to concrete entities. Philosophers, with the sole lancet of logic, are not equipped to deal with facts and should not try to compete with scientists. Philosophic analysis cannot properly deal with questions such as the actual usage of the word 'true' in English or in Maya (a problem belonging to linguistics) or with problems of psychology, such as perception. What is true is that no adequate theory of truth can dispense with a preliminary, prephilosophical, linguistic investigation into the actual usages of the word 'true,' just as no scientific epistemology can afford to ignore psychological discussions and findings concerning perception.

To philosophize directly about empirical objects, such as ordinary language (or sense perception, or monkeys), is methodologically as objectionable as to construct philosophies of nature without paying attention to the sciences of nature: it is an imitation of the Romantic *Naturphilosophie.*[3] This attitude has always proved sterile and will never be fruitful, because it rests on the false assumption that verbal distinctions and resemblances are the sole clues for solving philosophical problems, which, in turn, are thought to be linguistic puzzles. The existence of expressions such as "He must be at home"

[3] See M. Bunge, "¿Qué es la epistemología?," *Minerva,* 1 (1944), 27 and "Auge y fracaso de la filosofía de la naturaleza," *id.,* 1 (1944), 213.

does not tell us what physical necessity may be, just as becoming aware of the usages of the phrase 'the art of sewing' does not open the door to aesthetics. Language is sometimes a guide, but more often than not it needs to be tutored because it harbors bad logic and superseded beliefs. Dealing with words alone may constitute a harmless mania or a dangerous return to scholasticism.

Philosophic analysis, if deep and fruitful, presupposes not only logic but also a body of information and theories. Although analysis is in a sense the opposite of theory building, a scientific philosophic analysis will presuppose, rather than oppose, a body of scientific information and theory. Not only will the very object of analysis—the analysandum—often be a theory, but the analysis itself will be performed in some cognitive context. And since we can choose between the context of ordinary knowledge and that of scientific knowledge, it is difficult to understand why the former should be preferred.

Mathematics and factual science stand midway between ordinary knowledge (expressed by means of ordinary language) and the highly artificial systems, such as many-valued logic, of which some logicians are so fond. Between the wealthy but confused and, in many ways, superficial daily parlance, on the one hand, and the neat but often poor and shallow, artificial languages which logicians can build without limitations, we find the not so neat but conceptually richer—and, above all, growing—systems of mathematics and factual science. The concepts, hypotheses, theories, and methods of mathematics and science are the objects, or analysanda, of *metascientific analysis*. Metascientific analysis, a part of the practice of metascience,[4] attempts to disclose the structure, meaning, and function of scientific terms, statements, systems, and patterns of procedure.

Metascientific analysis is not popular among illuministic

[4] The prefix 'meta' is short for 'theory of,' or simply 'about,' and has nothing to do, in this context, with 'beyond.' Thus *metascience* designates the union of the philosophy and the methodology of science. See M. Bunge, *Metascientific Queries* (Springfield, Ill.: Charles C. Thomas, Publisher, 1959), Chapter 1.

(non-obscurantist) philosophers, who for the most part prefer either ordinary analysis or the construction of extremely artificial systems whereby nonfutile problems are bypassed rather than solved. There is a danger in this kind of isolation of philosophy from the rich and changing world of extraphilosophic ideas—a danger similar to the one faced by diplomats. A career diplomat is said to be a person who is interested solely in what his colleagues may whisper to him: he will not take the trouble of learning about the world in which he lives. Some career philosophers are like diplomats, in that they are receptive only of what their colleagues, both present and past, have to say; they will be deaf to the world. In particular, they will be deaf to the world of science—that restless, almost radioactive nucleus of modern culture.[5] They will not be interested in metascientific analysis; nor will scientists take an interest in their extrascientific analyses. In such a situation we see one more feature of the gap between the humanistic and the scientific cultures.

Philosophic analysis can be boring or interesting, futile or challenging, unilluminating or instructive, parochial or wide-embracing, untranslatable into other tongues or universal, sterile or fruitful. It all will depend upon its analysandum, or problem, and upon the tools of analysis. And the choice of either the subject of analysis or its method will depend upon the desiderata or aims of analysis itself, to which I now turn.

## 3. *Aims of Philosophical Analysis*

Philosophic analysis may be analyzed not only with respect to subject matter and tools but also with regard to aims. A

[5] See, e.g., the modest and, at the same time, revealing and appalling confession of G. E. Moore, the founder of the so-called Oxford philosophy, in his "Autobiography," in P. A. Schilpp (Ed.), *The Philosophy of G. E. Moore* (Chicago: Northwestern University, Library of Living Philosophers, 1942), p. 14: "I do not think that the world or the sciences would ever have suggested to me any philosophical problems. What has suggested philosophical problems to me is things which other philosophers have said about the world or the sciences."

possible analysis in this respect is the classification of kinds of analysis into dissolution, trivialization, reduction, and elucidation.[6]

### 3.1. *Dissolution*

The refusal to handle certain concepts will automatically dissolve certain problems. Thus if the notion of reality is declared spurious or at least suspect (and a term such as 'actuality' is recognized as a hypocritical substitute for it), the problems of distinguishing appearances from reality, and of ascertaining whether the referents of theoretical constructs are real, will be branded as pseudoproblems, and the attempts to deal with them will be stigmatized as metaphysical.

But it can be argued that some pseudoproblems are more interesting than any cleanly stated but futile problems. Moreover, 'pseudo-problem' may designate an ill-stated question, or a question for which no possible answer can be given, but it may also designate a query that is dismissed because it is embarrassing for some dogma; the latter belongs to the class of pseudopseudoproblems. A genuine pseudoproblem is "In what does the being of nothingness reside?" An instance of a pseudopseudoproblem might be "What is time, apart from considerations concerning time-measuring devices?" This is a pseudoproblem in the context of subjectivism (and particularly operationism), but not necessarily in other contexts as well.

Dissolving analysis can be conducted properly or improperly: in the first case it will clean up some of the debris inherited from precritical thinking and noncritical uses of language. But it may also obstruct research by outlawing genuine queries or by laughing at ill-posed yet deep questions instead of trying to restate them correctly. Dissolving analysis must, therefore, be performed with care: a handful of pseudoproblems may be less dangerous than the killing of a single genuine problem.

[6] For a different, and remarkably lucid analysis, see J. O. Urmson, *Philosophical Analysis* (Oxford: Clarendon Press, 1956).

### 3.2. *Trivialization*

A deep thought is trivialized in the attempt to explain it to a child; complex and rich concepts, such as 'possibility,' 'causation,' or 'truth,' will be trivialized by extruding them from their technical contexts. The most effective procedure of trivialization is the conversion of conceptual analysis into linguistic description.

Thus if someone asks "What is time?" the trivializer will direct him to ponder over phrases like "What time is it?," "It is bed-time," "Time is money," and so forth. Notice, first, that the method cannot be exported: when translated into other languages, some such questions lose the word 'time,' which is often translated into 'hour.' Verbophile analysis, being hardly translatable, is as parochial as the existentialist philological games; and, not being universal, it is not philosophical. In the second place, the questions of physical, physiological, and psychological time will then be avoided, and time as an ontological category will be left unanalyzed: only a description of actual and ordinary usages of the word 'time' in a given linguistic community (say, in some Oxford colleges) will be supplied. And no ingenuity will make up for the loss of depth and universality.

Trivializing analysis is nonscientific: it relies chiefly on the personal and ordinary experience of the enquirer; it makes no use of interviews, questionnaires, statistical processing of data, history, and so forth. A philosophical question—e.g., the nature of time—is transformed into an empirical question (namely, finding out certain patterns of verbal behavior), but the empirical problem is not approached in a scientific mood, as empirical questions are supposed to be in modern culture.

No doubt, philosophy comes down within the reach of the masses if philosophical problems are trivialized. But the masses would gain much more if they learned to taste genuine philosophy.

### 3.3. *Reduction*

Every analysis is, in a sense, a reduction, that is, a decomposition of a complex into simpler units and a disclosure of a mesh of relations. The reduction of concepts may be direct or indirect. Explicit nominal definition is a way of achieving reduction directly, and "constitution" [7] is a way of achieving it indirectly.

Thus one can say that the explicit definition of *C* in terms of *A* and *B*—e.g., in the form "Something is a *C* if and only if it is both *A* and *B*"—in a sense reduces the concept *C* to the concepts *A* and *B*, as when 'one' is defined as the successor of zero. And a concept *C* is said to be "constituted" out of (or reduced to) the concepts *A* and *B* if all propositions concerning *C* can be translated into propositions containing *A* and *B*, as when propositions regarding fractionary numbers are translated into propositions concerning integers. Similarly, a reduction of propositions is performed whenever complex or molecular sentences are shown to be composed of simple or atomic sentences.

The constitution or logical construction of concepts has largely succeeded in mathematics through the set-theoretical foundation of mathematical theories. But constitution does not seem as promising in the factual sciences which, far from enjoying the freedom of mathematics, have to account for a world existing on its own, organized in qualitatively different levels and having, to all appearances, no ultimate basement built out of irreducible bricks. In science the disclosure of relations and connections has proved more fruitful than the search for primary, irreducible units. The unity of science lies in its method rather than in a handful of all-purpose concepts.

Of course, it is possible to attempt the "constitution" of physical object terms, such as 'thing' and 'event,' in terms of allegedly unanalyzable units, such as "the simplest elements of

[7] See R. Carnap, *Der logische Aufbau der Welt* (Berlin: Weltkreis, 1928), sec. 1. Incidentally, the Preface to this work is still an admirable manifesto of scientific philosophy.

our perceptual knowledge" or in terms of human operations.[8] But in such a case the analysis is not made for the sake of gaining insight and clarity but, chiefly, to gratify both some subjectivist epistemology and the metaphysical yearnings for an ontological reduction of everything to some basic units. Far from being a purely technical matter, analysis becomes then the tool of school philosophy.

The troubles with such particular applications of logical analysis to metaphysics are: (*a*) they are made outside of science, usually in the context of some subjectivistic (e.g., phenomenalistic or operationistic) theory; (*b*) they take as basic atoms what both physics and psychology show to be enormously complex entities, namely, phenomena; (*c*) there is no evidence of the existence of absolute ultimates or irreducible "simple natures" in reality: the stopping of analysis at a given stage may be a symptom of our own poverty rather than an evidence of the analysandum's simplicity; (*d*) they are misleading, because science begins precisely where the subject-centered language of perception (i.e., the phenomenalist language) fails to account for the world: science transcends and explains what is given in experience rather than remaining limited to it.

Reductive analysis, in short, is fruitful as long as it is logical rather than ontological and as long as it is not made to serve philosophical tenets, such as phenomenalism, that are uncongenial with science.

[8] This way of construing logical construction was proposed by B. Russell in "The Relation of Sense-Data to Physics" (1914), repr. in *Mysticism and Logic* (London: George Allen & Unwin, 1917). Russell abandoned it a few years later. The phenomenalistic programme was further pursued by A. N. Whitehead, *An Enquiry Concerning the Principles of Natural Knowledge* (Cambridge: University Press, 1919), R. Carnap, *op. cit.* (in fn. 7), and N. Goodman, *The Structure of Appearance* (Cambridge, Mass.: Harvard University Press, 1951). This programme had been anticipated, at the turn of the century, by G. Kirchhoff, E. Mach, W. Ostwald, K. Pearson, and P. Duhem. The whole programme of phenomenalistic reduction was at variance with modern science, which is diaphenomenalistic or realistic. Regressive as these attempts are in science, they have been revolutionary in philosophy as a first attempt to apply the exact techniques of logic and a sober scientific spirit to epistemological and ontological questions.

### 3.4. *Elucidation*

Elucidation or clarification embraces what is legitimate, or fruitful, in reduction. Some degree of elucidation is achieved by analyzing propositions into their elementary constituents, as in the case of '$r \equiv p \,\&\, q$'; by showing their internal structure, as when "Some gases are heavier than air" is shown to be of the form $(\exists x)(Gx \,\&\, xHa)$'; by defining some concepts in terms of further concepts which are taken as primitive in the given context (without, however, any implications of physical or ontological irreducibility); by explaining or specifying the meanings of primitives with the help of examples and rules of interpretation; by classifying and ordering; by digging up some of the presuppositions of key hypotheses, theories, and rules; by laying bare the practical import of some assumptions; and by showing the task certain statements and theories perform.

Elucidating analysis is syntactical or formal, semantical, epistemological, and pragmatic. It dissolves some pseudoquestions, solves some problems, and raises others; it provides translations into more intelligible expressions and (when required) into testable assumptions, and it shows hidden structures and functions. The chief aim of this kind of analysis is the clarification of concepts, hypotheses, theories, and methods. If performed upon an analysandum relevant to science, in the light of scientific information, and with the tools of scientific philosophy, elucidation boils down to metascientific *analysis,* as characterized in sec. 2.

Now, elucidation may be achieved through exemplification, analysis, or synthesis. Let us deal with the latter.

## 4. *Elucidation Through Construction*

If someone asks what the meaning of the term 'gravitational field intensity' is, the most rigorous answer—though certainly not the most commendable from a didactic point of view—is to exhibit, discuss, and apply the basic equations of some theory of the gravitational field. An *exact* and *consistent* use of concepts is impossible in the context of ordinary knowledge, with its superficiality, haziness, and inconsistencies; a precise specification of meaning is possible only through systematization or theorification, i.e., through incorporation or expansion of the concept, as the case may be, into a theory.

The most rigorous systematization is, of course, formalization, i.e., axiomatization plus explicit exhibition of presuppositions and rules.[9] All other devices—such as explicit definition, linguistic analysis, and so on—are obviously inapplicable to the primitive concepts of mathematics and science. Unfortunately, formalization is almost unattainable outside a few fields (notably the formal sciences), and even in these it cannot hope to be exhaustive. On the other hand, direct and precise elucidation is rarely if ever indispensable, because every statement contributes, if only a little, to specify the meaning of the terms it contains.

Now elucidation through theorification can be made either by an analysis of an existing theory or by building a new theory, depending on whether or not the term or phrase to be elucidated is accurately and consistently used in some moderately satisfactory theory. If the theory is satisfactory in some respect but still too imperfect in others, or the use is much too indefinite, it will be worthwhile to attempt the construction of a new theory—an enterprise usually undertaken with the aim of extending or deepening our knowledge rather than for the sake of clarifying some term. Thus the best way of elucidating the elusive concept of a fundamental particle would be to build a moderately adequate theory embracing all the known kinds of the so-called fundamental particles; and the most effective manner of elucidating the equally difficult concept of testability would be to construct a quantitative theory of degrees of testability.

If the term to be elucidated is relevant to science and the

[9] This idea was first systematically exploited by A. Tarski in "The Concept of Truth in Formalized Languages" (1931), repr. in *Logic, Semantics, Metamathematics*, transl. J. H. Woodger (Oxford: Clarendon Press, 1956).

task of systematization is made in a way congenial with science and scientific philosophy, elucidation may deserve the name of *metascientific synthesis.* Unlike metascientific analysis, metascientific synthesis may introduce some change in the meaning of the elucidandum. While analysis turns $C$ into, say, $A$ & $B$, theorification may turn the given, presystematic $C$ into a $C_t$ having a family resemblance to $C$, which now becomes a poor relative, as in the case of the everyday term 'force' in relation to the corresponding mechanical concept of force. In other words, elucidation through synthesis may be creative and has, therefore, better chances of constituting an addition to knowledge. This may be one motive for more and more logicians and metascientists preferring theory construction to theory analysis.

In constructing a theory which aims chiefly at elucidating a concept or a whole family of concepts, the pitfall of artificiality should be avoided; that is, the new concept, $C_t$, introduced by the theory, should not be altogether alien to the concept $C$ that it is supposed to elucidate or reconstruct in a systematic way. It must be possible to recognize in $C_t$ at least a good imitation of $C$. Otherwise the whole theory may be useless and even misleading. (On the other hand, if the aim of theorizing is scientific rather than metascientific, the theoretician will be free to introduce any radically new concept, with no presystematic antecedent, the only restriction being that it occur in ultimately testable formulas.)

Suppose someone wishes to perform an elucidation, through systematization or construction, of a term such as 'analytic sentence,' 'scientific law,' or 'degree of truth.' If he is an advocate of ordinary language philosophy he will be at a loss, because these terms hardly occur in ordinary discourse. A partisan of constructivism, on the other hand, would proceed to concoct a system (sometimes called language) in which the term in question occurred essentially, whether as a primitive or as a defined term.

Now the concocted system that allows the synthetic elucidation of the given term may be imposing at first sight, but very often it will be much simpler (i.e., poorer) than any actual scientific theory. For instance, it will allow only one-place predicates, all of them nonmetrical, like 'is blue,' which apply to a finite universe of individuals, preferably concrete. In other words, the system will most likely be highly artificial, much too simple to meet the requirements of science. An elucidation is certainly achieved in this way, but what clarity is gained stems from the exaggerated poverty of the system. The gap between the original concept $C$ and the theorified concept $C_t$ will be too large, and the whole theory, no matter how rigorously it has been built, will be of little use as a tool for elucidation.

The complexities—and the ensuing perplexities—of real languages and theories are avoided by the construction of such simple, highly artificial, though logically unimpeachable systems. By the same token the original problem—the elucidation of a technical term already in use—has been bypassed. We are not told, e.g., what analytic sentences, scientific laws, or degrees of truth are: we are only given more or less artificial *stipulations* that specify the meanings of entirely *new* concepts, even though they may be designated by the same signs. If we are not aware of such a difference, confusion rather than clarification may ensue.

Artificial constructivism reminds one of the judge who, upon being asked to do justice to a plaintiff, replied: "Suppose the plaintiff lived in Utopia. Then his case would easily be solved by merely complying with his request, since in Utopia every wish is fulfilled. As things are, I must rule to dismiss the case." Neither linguistic analysis nor extreme constructivism are concerned with key concepts of science and philosophy such as they occur in existing theories. Contemporary system builders too often resemble classical system builders as regards artificiality, though not, of course, as regards rigor. Artificial constructivism is a school of rigor and ingenuity even if it is other-worldly.

Artificiality is not easy to avoid. Metascientific synthesis is not unlike the solving of engineering problems: in either case one attempts to build a beautiful theory concerning an ugly piece of reality, or to construct an efficient tool with the help of an ugly theory. To make both ends meet is very difficult—but this makes the enterprise that much more interesting.

### 5. *Elucidation and the Scientific Reconstruction of Philosophy*

Unfortunately for modern culture, too many philosophers fall into one of these categories: the satiate, the hungry but toothless, and the toothed without appetite. The satiate are those who are basically satisfied with some school (or church or party) philosophy and are only concerned with "applying" it, by exhibiting more and more alleged confirmations, both in order to strengthen the faith and crush the unbelievers. They think, and rightly so, that the only way of preserving a perennial philosophy is to keep it in the freezer; consequently they resist every change in problems, approaches, and theories.

The hungry but toothless philosophers are those who wrestle with genuine problems concerning being, knowing, and valuating, but are not equipped with the powerful techniques of contemporary philosophic analysis and synthesis. Hence they are too often unable even to state their problems meaningfully and to take advantage of the progress of knowledge.

Finally, the toothed but inappetent philosophers are those who are technically well equipped but are interested neither in those problems inherited from classical philosophy which are genuine and remain unsolved, nor in the new problems posed every day by the advancement of knowledge. As a consequence, they spend too much of their time with inventing and working out ingenious little problems of the type of "What if mice became cats when locked in lead closets and were metamorphosed again into mice upon opening the closets?" Such questions may constitute classroom exercises, but they hardly ever contribute to the progress of philosophy, a progress which is possible and desirable as soon as philosophy is done in a scientific spirit.

All philosophic schools nowadays are dead or dying, as witnessed by their impotence to propose new problems, new approaches, and new theories. Yet in spite of this the output of new philosophic problems, approaches, and theories is now higher than ever: philosophy is being reconstructed outside of the schools. True enough, the reconstruction is much too slow, partly because many of the builders are well-toothed but feel no appetite for the rich material afforded by the rest of culture.

So far, the reconstruction of philosophy along scientific lines has been approached in the field of logic alone, with a well-known and wonderful success. Epistemology and ontology are still waiting, partly because most of the philosophers of the *nouvelle vague* are still under the spell of anachronistic and sterile tenets, such as radical empiricism, inductivism, and simplicism. Some progress has undoubtedly been made in these fields. In the first place, the mere use of modern logic and the avoidance of mysticism and intuitionism constitute definite advances. In the second place, some traditional problems of epistemology, such as the problem of truth, have been taken up by philosophical semantics, and the logical analysis of experiential data has been sketched.[10] Yet in these new approaches to important and old problems of philosophy insufficient attention is paid to the methods and philosophical needs of science.

Epistemology and ontology will remain in their present underdeveloped state unless philosophers succeed in matching a rigorous approach with a wise selection of problems, such as those concerning the basic traits of the world, the advancement of knowledge, and the nature of theoretical science. And a prerequisite of a wise selection of problems is the dissolution of the unholy alliance between new methods and old myths, such as the Myth of the Pure Datum, the Myth of Induction, the Myth of Reduction, the Myth of Ultimate Constituents, and the Myth of Simplicity.

[10] For a representative sample of semantics see L. Linsky (Ed.), *Semantics and the Philosophy of Language* (Urbana: University of Illinois Press, 1952). Concerning the logical analysis of ordinary (nonscientific) experience, see footnote 8.

Ontology is particularly in need of a new look, and it will achieve it with the help of metascientific analysis and synthesis, even though the old guard metaphysician feels that ontology is utterly incompatible with anything smacking of science. The job of analysis, whether logical or chemical, is to discern variety in unity, just as the concern of ontology is to disclose unity in diversity and, consequently, to build theories accounting for the basic traits of that unit of units, the universe. Analysis starts from unity, ontology from plurality; and scientific ontology will start from the plurality furnished by contemporary factual science—unlike old-fashioned ontologies, which in the best of cases drew upon outdated science.

Unity and variety are to be distinguished in thought, but are not separate *in re*. A lump of matter, an event, a reasoning, or a concept does not cease to be a unit in some respects or at certain levels because we succeed in showing its complexity; and the various parts of a unit are not effaced because we discover their interrelations and unity in some respect. Philosophic analysis and ontology are not mutually incompatible but mutually complementary, like the tool and the raw material. Analysis by itself does not create theories, but it avoids nonsense. And this is particularly important when basic categories—such as time, space, matter, change, chance, or law—are at stake. Metascientific analysis and synthesis are inconsistent only with nonsense ontologies, not with ontology as such. If a land of opportunity remains, this is the land of scientific ontology conceived as a kind of superscience.

## 6. *Summary and Conclusions*

The disclosure of the structure and function of a piece of discourse is a work of analysis. The elucidation of meaning, on the other hand, is most accurately performed by constructing theories. But if in the process of analysis meanings may be made more definite, in the building of systems new meanings may be created.

Analysis and synthesis in the interest of elucidation—unlike dissolving, trivializing, and reductive analyses—do not result in an oversimplification of genuine issues. The kind of elucidation attempted by analysis and synthesis is of all these methods the most rewarding, especially when applied to significant problems, such as those which arise in thinking about mathematics and science. On the other hand, nothing exciting or fruitful can be expected from an analysis of ideas in the context of ordinary knowledge, even when that analysis is logically rigorous. Genuine and difficult problems do arise, however, when ordinary language is analyzed and gauged with the ruler of logic, when the latter is required to account for more shades of scientific language, when commonsense is analyzed in scientific terms or when its claims to incorrigibility and fundamentality are assessed.

Analysis and synthesis in philosophy are most fertile when they lead to a better understanding of knowledge, and knowledge is a clue to the understanding of both nature and culture. Metascientific elucidation—the clarification of ideas relevant to science, and done in a scientific mood—is interesting *per se,* as a technical contribution to philosophy, but it may also contribute to the cleansing and deepening of science itself. Thus, scientists alerted by metascience will not believe they define a term when they measure the property it designates; they will not be afraid of introducing transempirical concepts; and they will not shun the investigation into the intimate mechanism of events and processes for fear of the black box philosophy.

In addition, metascientific elucidation may be effective in a wider cultural circle by dissuading us from caging beliefs, from regimenting thought, and from harboring simplistic notions. Metascientific elucidation, whether analytic or synthetic, unveils complexities, even the complexity of notions such as that of simplicity.

# 2

# Analyticity

Let us begin our exercises in metascientific analysis with an examination of that stronghold of traditional rationalism—the class of propositions that can be supported and criticized by purely logical argument. This problem of analyticity is interesting—and fashionable—both because the class of analytic propositions is more extended and complex than is usually avowed, and because many statements that at first sight look synthetic, or arguable in empirical terms, are actually analytic in some sense.

An interesting case of disguised analyticity is that of the statement "Physical objects exist even when they are not perceived." This sentence is undoubtedly true; moreover it is analytically true, whence it cannot be adopted with profit as a postulate in a theory purporting to account for the world and its knowledge. It cannot even be rejected, because its denial would be a self-contradiction. In fact, 'physical object' is usually *defined* as that which has independent existence, so that the above sentence can be interpreted either as an indirect definition or as a tautology. Upon substitution of 'physical object' by its definiens we obtain the indubitable but unenlightening proposition "Objects which exist even when they are not perceived exist even when they are not perceived."

The complexity of the notion of analyticity has given rise to many arguments and misunderstandings. This chapter is an attempt to show how, just by recognizing the complexity of the concept, the whole discussion can be simplified, and perhaps even stopped. When a problem is suspected to have originated at least partly in a verbal muddle, it is allowable to attempt to clarify or even to dissolve it by proposing a redefinition of the key terms involved. Such a chaos, consisting in an unrecognized multiplicity of meanings of a key term, seems to exist in connection with our problem. Indeed, in many discussions on analyticity one gets the impression that one and the same author maintains overtly a Pickwickian definition of the predicate 'analytic' without actually abandoning another, wider meaning of the term, which remains hidden in the back of his mind—to wit, the etymological one of *decidable by rational examination alone.* Were this psychological diagnosis correct, then the overt recognition and adoption of this broader and lower-browed linguistic convention would be helpful, especially if the proposed redefinition were shown to contain the acknowledged connotations. What follows is a formal statement of this proposal and an enquiry into the consequences of its adoption.

## 1. *Redefinition of Analyticity*

I propose to redefine the predicate 'is analytic in *S*,' where '*S*' designates a linguistic or a cognitive system, as the genus of those expressions the truth value of which can be ascertained by their syntactical or semantical examination alone, i.e., by dispensing with empirical operations. (Analysis may require the employment of propositions belonging to the empirical sciences, but will not therefore be empirical.) More precisely, I propose the following definitions:

> *Df. 1.* An expression is analytic in *S* if and only if it can be validated or invalidated by means of an examination of its component signs, with the sole help of other expressions of *S* and/or the logic *L* presupposed by *S*.
>
> *Df. 2.* An expression is synthetic in *S* if and only if it is not analytic in *S*.

Notice that these redefinitions (*a*) involve a return to the etymology of 'analytic'; (*b*) relativize the notion of analyticity to a system instead of regarding it as a property inherent in propositions; (*c*) are methodological, since they stipulate that the assignment of the predicates 'is analytic' and 'is synthetic' should be based only on information regarding the procedures by which the expressions concerned are validated or invalidated.

If the above proposal were accepted we would have to acknowledge that the predicate 'is analytic' characterizes a genus embracing various species. Let us survey them.

## 2. *Kinds of Analyticity*

At least the following classes of analytic statements are consistent with the proposed definition.

I. *Tautologies,* or propositions true in *S* by virtue of their form and independently of their meaning. Synonyms: logical truths, syntactically analytic, or syntactically true, or extensionally true propositions.

Example: "Semantics is fertile or is not fertile" is a tautology relative to any *L* accepting the excluded middle law.

Recall that the truth of these complex propositions does not depend on the truth value of the component propositions. Only tautologies and their contradictories need be molecular in order to be analytic in the present classification.

II. *Contradictions,* or propositions false in *S* by virtue of their form and independently of their meaning. Synonyms: logical falsehoods, syntactically false, or extensionally false propositions.

Example: "Semantics is fertile and not fertile" is logically false relative to any *L* accepting the law of contradiction.

III. *Tautonymies,* or propositions true in *S* by virtue of the meanings of the terms occurring in them. Synonyms: semantical truths, semantically analytic, or semantically true, or intensionally true propositions.

Examples: "Bachelors are unmarried" is a tautonymy in English. "All Indians are born in India" was a tautonymy in the context of pre-Columbian geography.

It may be noticed that what are here called tautonymies could be regarded as semantical rules in disguise; the difference between tautonymies and rules of designation is that the former are linguistic conventions taking the form of propositions, not of proposals (such as "Let '*S*' designate a linguistic or a cognitive system.") Notice further that a tautonymy does not necessarily establish a *synonymy*. Thus, in the tautonymy "Chronometers are time-measuring instruments," the predicates 'chronometer' and 'time-measuring instrument' have neither the same connotation nor the same denotation, so that they are not exchangeable. Whence the proposition does not exemplify analyticity in the Frege-Russell sense.

IV. *Heteronymies,* or propositions false in *S* by virtue of the meanings of the term entering into them. Synonyms: semantical falsehoods, or semantically false, or intensionally false propositions.

Example: "Induction is a kind of demonstrative inference" is heteronymous. On the other hand "Electrons are virtuous" is just meaningless in the context of physics, and empirically false in the context of descriptive ethics, since 'virtue' is characterized in terms of a class of norms of behavior, which electrons are not even entitled to violate.

V. *Axioms true by convention,* or propositions both basic and true in *S* by virtue of stipulations. Synonyms: conventional postulates, or truths by stipulations.

Examples: the postulates of logic and pure mathematics.

It should be unnecessary to insist that the postulates that are introduced by convention are not arbitrarily posited, but are chosen because of their expected fruitfulness, systematizing power, and convenience. They are analytic according to Df. 1 because their status is automatically recognized in every axiomatic *S*, merely by looking at its list of undemonstrated assumptions.

VI. *Explicit analytic definitions,* or synonymies in *S* that are not proposals.

Example: "$x$ is a philosopher if and only if $x$ poses, solves, or dissolves philosophical problems" is an analytic definition of 'philosopher.' (This example shows, by the way, how naive the contention is that analytic sentences are all noncommittal. Any amount of venom can be poured into an analytic definition concerning humans.)

In contrast with tautonymies (see class III above), explicit analytic definitions establish strict synonymies and can consequently be used as rules of elimination (of the defined terms). Notice that, in contrast with syntactical conventions, definitions of this sort are full-fledged propositions, whence they are true or false.

VII. *Definitional descriptions,* or definitional name-term relations.

Examples: "Philoloafers are those who lead an idle life" is a definitional description in any linguistic system willing to accept the neologism 'philoloafer.' "One metre is the ten-millionth part of a quarter of terrestrial meridian" was a (true by convention) definitional description in the context in which the decimal metric system was first formulated.

VIII. *Definitional truths,* or propositions true in $S$ either because they are implicit definitions, or recursive definitions, or because they are derivable with the sole help of explicit definitions and truths of logic.

Examples: "$(n + 0 = n)$ & $(n \cdot 0 = 0)$," an implicit definition of zero, is analytic in systems of arithmetic which do not take zero as a primitive. "7 is a prime number" can be recognized as true in ordinary arithmetic by means of the sole definition of 'prime number.' "Pure water boils at 100°C at normal pressure" is analytic in physics if the centigrade scale is adopted, since it is an implicit definition of the fixed point 100°C. "Change is inherent in every living society" is likewise analytic because it can be derived from the explicit definition "A society is alive if and only if it changes."

IX. *Designational truths,* or truths derivable in $S$ with the sole help of rules of designation belonging to $S$ and truths of logic.

Example: "The trout is a swimming animal" is analytic in every $S$ containing the following rules of designation: " 'Trout' designates a fish," and " 'Fish' designates a swimming animal."

Notice that the truths we are calling designational are not tautonymies although some of them can be derived from tautonymies.

X. *Demonstrable theorems,* or propositions true in $S$ because they are deducible from the principles and definitions of $S$ with the help of $L$.

Example: "*Homo sapiens* has evolved by natural selection" is a theorem of evolutionary biology.

A closer examination might discern further kinds of analyticity, or lead to the merging of some which are here distinguished.

### 3. *Contextual Nature of Analyticity*

It has been assumed in the foregoing that analyticity is a contextual predicate, that is, a property of propositions relative to the system in which they occur, whence we should write '$A(p,S)$' rather than '$A(p)$.' Let us examine this assumption.

I. *Tautology*. A change in the logic $L$ presupposed by $S$ may suffice to expel some propositions from the class of tautologies. For instance, "$p$ or not-$p$" need not be tautological in many-valued logical calculi and is not one of the tautologies of intuitionistic logic.[1]

II. *Contradiction*. The same as for I. (Remember the systems of Indian and Chinese logic which are sometimes said to accept contradictions—not to mention Hegel and his followers.)

III. *Tautonymy*. A change in the cognitive situation may alter the status of a tautonymy in $S$. For instance, "All Indians are born in India" is no longer tautonymous in the context of our present knowledge.

IV. *Heteronymy*. The same as for III.

V. *Axiom true by convention*. Any change in the postulational basis of a theory involves the dethronement of some of its axioms. For example, "Everything green is extended" is analytic in any system containing the axiom "Everything colored is extended," but may be synthetic in alternative systems. No proposition is intrinsically axiomatic or theorematic, and no truth is intrinsically conventional or demonstrated.

VI. *Explicit analytic definition*. The definition of 'philosopher' as one who poses, solves, and dissolves philosophical problems, might be the outcome of an empirical research about the peculiar activities of men who are regarded as philosophers on different counts, e.g., because their names occur in histories of philosophy.

VII. *Definitional description*. The original definition of the metre is now a synthetic (and false) proposition. "Matter is that which exists objectively" is analytic as regarded as a definition of 'matter'; it would become synthetic if the meaning of the

[1] For an examination of some problems concerning the excluded middle and intuitionistic logic, see M. Bunge, *Intuition and Science* (Englewood Cliffs, N. J.: Prentice-Hall, Inc., 1962), Chapter 2, sec. 2.

definiendum were specified in terms of predicates other than 'objective existence.'

VIII. *Definitional truth.* A change in some definitions, or the extrusion from *S* of some terms, are enough for the vanishing of some definitional truths. Thus, "When an invention is premature, it is either ignored or rejected" (a proposition which has been proposed as a law of history), is simply meaningless in the context of a theory of history that does not admit invention, but only discovery and/or imitation. "Surviving organisms are the fittest in the struggle for life" may be regarded as an implicit definition of 'fitness' in terms of 'survival' and 'struggle for life'; but if fitness were independently defined or characterized, we would gain a law of biology in the place of a truth of reason.

IX. *Designational truth.* Since the status of these propositions depends on the semantical rules of *S*, it is obvious that a change in the latter may deanalyticize some former designational truths.

X. *Demonstrable theorems.* The same as for V.

To sum up, the thesis of the contextual nature of analyticity seems to have been justified. 'Analytic' and 'synthetic' are not attributes inherent in isolated propositions but are relational, contextual, systemic properties, relative to the system in which the expressions under examination occur. Generalizing, no formula has an intrinsic logical status: what it *is* depends on what it *does* or, better, on what we do with it; and its functions are dependent on our aims with regard to the particular linguistic or cognitive situation in which the formula occurs.

## 4. *The Analytic / Synthetic Dichotomy*

If analyticity is contextual, then the analytic/synthetic dichotomy is contextual as well. In other words, a change in context may force us to alter the validation procedure, hence to shift the barrier between the analytic and the synthetic. For instance, instead of performing empirical operations we may have to perform linguistic (syntactic and/or semantic) analyses.

The analytic/synthetic dichotomy is therefore relative but not foolish: it is perfectly valid in each context and it must be kept if we do not wish to confuse empirical with linguistic problems and procedures. The elementary laws of ordinary arithmetic and geometry began their existence as humble synthetic propositions concerning material objects and were found with the help of empirical procedures, such as counting and measuring; it was only after thousands of years that they acquired the respectable status of analytic statements. Galileo's law of falling bodies was likewise synthetic and a posteriori when it was first formulated. Since Newton's work it has become analytic (in our extended sense of the term), because it is derivable from propositions belonging to a higher level of theory. But, of course, Galileo's law has not become a priori: it is both analytic and a posteriori, as will be argued in the next section. This may be shocking because unusual, but it is not incongruous: Galileo's law is *logically* analytic and epistemologically a posteriori.

The relativization of the distinction between the analytic and the synthetic makes their *rigid* distinction untenable, as has been noted before by several authors on various grounds.[2] But the distinction, which is indispensable,[3] is not therefore

[2] M. White, "The Analytic and the Synthetic: An Untenable Dualism" (1950), reprinted in L. Linsky (Ed.), *Semantics and the Philosophy of Language* (Urbana: University of Illinois Press, 1952). W. V. Quine, "Two Dogmas of Empiricism" (1951), reprinted in *From a Logical Point of View* (Cambridge, Mass.: Harvard University Press, 1953). W. Sellars, "Is There a Synthetic A Priori?" (1953), reprinted in S. Hook (Ed.), *American Philosophers at Work* (New York: Criterion Books, Inc., 1956). K. Ajdukiewicz, "Le problème du fondement des propositions analytiques," *Studia Logica*, 8 (1958), 259. M. Bunge, *Metascientific Queries* (Springfield, Ill.: Charles C. Thomas, Publisher, 1959), Chapter 3.

[3] H. Feigl, "The Philosophy of Science of Logical Empiricism," in *Proceedings of the Second International Congress of the International Union for the Philosophy of Science* (Neuchâtel: Ed. du Griffon, 1955), I, 95.

erased. Generalizing, one may say that the rational and the empirical are different but, far from being absolutely determined, are relative to the total cognitive situation (background body of knowledge, validation procedures, etc.)

A further consequence of our redefinition of 'analytic' and 'synthetic' is that not only synthetic propositions are informative: analytic a posteriori propositions, such as the theorems of factual science, are informative as well. Hence, 'synthetic' and 'informative' should not be regarded as synonymous if the proposed redefinition of analyticity is accepted. Not even nominal definitions are pragmatically void, although they are factually empty: in fact, at the pragmatic level every nominal definition functions as a rule for the use and, particularly, for the substitution of signs, whence it has a definite pragmatic content.

This is true of every syntactic formula: even if devoid of meaning and reference, an abstract formula may be employed as a rule stipulating the handling of the signs involved—which does not imply that every formula is nothing but a rule. Think of the statement "$(x)(y)(xRy = yRx)$" with unspecified individuals $x$, $y$ and an unspecified dyadic operation $R$. Expressions of this form are found in certain abstract (uninterpreted) mathematical theories such as group theory. They are therefore analytic in our enlarged sense of 'analytic'; they are moreover meaningless, yet they partially specify the mode of operating with the sign '$R$.'

## 5. *Analyticity and the A Priori*

It is customary to call a priori those propositions which are independent of fact; in particular, those which are true "come what may," as Quine would say; or, as Lewis said, those which are true or false "no matter what." (It may be argued that aprioriness is as relative to the cognitive situation as analyticity, but this need not concern us here.) If the redefinition of analyticity proposed above is accepted, a change in the traditional associations of the logical predicate 'analytic' with the epistemological predicate 'a priori' ensues.

In fact, besides analytic a priori, synthetic a priori, and synthetic a posteriori propositions, a possibility that seems to be absent from the philosophical literature appears, namely that of *analytic a posteriori* propositions. Indeed, as was mentioned in connection with Galileo's law of falling bodies, a proposition may be analytic in a given *S* while being at the same time a posteriori, because the statements from which it is derived are not independent of experience for their validation, i.e., they are not true come what may. This situation is common in theoretical physics, where all the propositions that have a reference are a posteriori in the sense that (*a*) they are neither posited arbitrarily nor obtained by precognition, and (*b*) they are supposed to be more or less true to fact as tested by experiment. At the same time, most of these statements (the theorems) are analytic in the system (theory) in which they occur in the sense that, given the axioms, definitions, and rules of transformation of the theory, the theorems are found, and their truth value is checked, by pencil and paper operations only. Of course, some (not all) of these theorems are also empirically validated; but this only shows that they are a posteriori, not that they are synthetic in our extended sense of the term. This situation would not look paradoxical were it not for (*a*) the current, but wrong, belief that all the theorems of theoretical science are empirically validated, and (*b*) the persistent confusion between the logical predicate 'is analytic' and the epistemological predicate 'is a priori.'

Generalizing, the theorems derivable from axioms of systems *S* of factual science are both analytic and a posteriori in *S*. Analytic a posteriori propositions are formally true and empirically more or less likely, i.e., true to some degree. This sort of double (or, rather, one and a half) truth is our best warrant for adopting them—until new notice.[4] Note that, although all

[4] See Chapter 8.

a priori propositions are analytic, the converse is not true. A posteriori analyticity may be offered as a consolation to those who still deplore the loss of synthetic a priori judgments—an irreversible loss indeed.

Now, if analyticity is marriageable to aposterioriness, then 'synthetic' should no longer be regarded as synonymous with 'a posteriori.' There are informative propositions having a factual (in particular, empirical) content which are analytic in certain theoretical contexts: they are not untouchable truths, external to the truths of reason, but are, so to speak, rational truths of fact.[5]

## 6. *Between Ordinary Language and Artificial System*

Our proposal is unlikely to attract either of the two extremes of contemporary analytic philosophy, who are concerned respectively with the description of ordinary uses of words and with the construction of highly artificial systems. (See Chapter 1.)

What has been redefined above is the notion of analytic sentence, not the concept of analytically *true* sentence. It may be objected[6] that this constitutes a violation of usage, which has consecrated the subsumption of analyticity under truth; that is, most people would regard analytic sentences as a subclass of the class of true sentences. My rejoinder is that there *is* no uniform and consistent usage of 'analytic,' and that this is why so many word wars have been waged around the term. But even if there were an established or at least a typical usage, it would be worthwhile to examine whether it is the *correct* usage, i.e., whether it does meet relevant logical and psychological standards.

A second possible objection is to the subsumption, in the view expounded above, of logical truth under analytic truth.

[5] M. Bunge, *Causality: The Place of the Causal Principle in Modern Science* (Cambridge, Mass.: Harvard University Press, 1959), 12.4.2.

[6] The objection has actually been made to me by Prof. G. Ryle in a kind personal communication.

True, the distinction between logical truth and analytic truth is dispensable in *formalized* systems, where everything is disciplined under the rules of logic and semantics.[7] But the distinction is convenient everywhere else, that is, in the vast majority of cases. And this leads us to the problem of elucidating the notion of analyticity through construction (see Chapter 1, sec. 4).

The most refined procedure for defining 'analytic truth' relative to a language presupposes the complete formulation of the syntax and the semantics of that language. But two objections to this procedure come to mind. First, one needs an elucidation of analyticity capable of functioning as a criterion for the distinction between analytic and synthetic sentences in *natural,* incompletely formalized languages, where the distinction is often blurred. Artificial languages are too ethereal to be utilizable on working days, but overalls need not be dirty. Second, since only a few logical and mathematical theories are entirely formalized (e.g., elementary logic, set theory, and group theory), we face the paradox that we have rigorous procedures for recognizing analyticity on condition that we deal with what is *known* to be analytic.[8] The refinements of philosophic Cubism are not more helpful than the roughness of philosophic Populism. If it had to depend on either, science would dwell in a logical wilderness.

## 7. *Conclusions*

The etymological and methodological redefinition of 'analytic' proposed at the outset of this chapter has the following advantages:

(1) It is *psychologically* simpler than the usual definitions;

[7] See R. Martin, *The Notion of Analytic Truth* (Philadelphia: Pennsylvania University Press, 1959), p. 42.

[8] An even more paradoxical situation is encountered when 'analytic' is equated with 'demonstrable,' as is the case with Martin's system referred to in footnote 7; for then all axioms, including those of logic and mathematics, are non-analytic, i.e., synthetic.

hence, it might contribute to simplifying the statement of a problem that has become enormously entangled.

(2) It is *open,* in the sense that it allows for further kinds of analytic propositions, according as new techniques of rational analysis are invented, or as they are discerned in current research. (After all, my pointing out precisely ten kinds of analyticity might be accounted for by a confessed bias in favor of the decimal system.)

(3) It *relativizes* the distinction between 'analytic' and 'synthetic' while preserving it for varying contexts.

(4) It *reduces vagueness* in the treatment of the analytic/synthetic problem, by dispensing with phrases like "true in all possible worlds"—or its post-Leibnizian equivalents in terms of state-descriptions—which are often employed to characterize analytic propositions.

(5) It allows us to *unambiguously decide* whether the predicate 'analytic' can be attributed to a proposition in a given context, because it does not contain vague phrases like 'in all possible cases' and does not make unrealistic demands upon our cognitive powers (like that of supplying a complete "state description" of the universe concerned), but requires only information about the validation method that has actually been employed with success.

(6) It applies to syntactical and semantical systems of *all kinds,* in every stage of formalization.

It will be noticed further that, according to the discussion in the preceding sections, if the proposed redefinition is accepted it follows that:

(1) The predicate 'true' cannot be attributed to propositions in isolation; a knowledge of the body of knowledge relevant to the proposition concerned is required, and since that body is changing the decision may not be final.

(2) Most of the propositions belonging to scientific theories become analytic in one of the senses distinguished above: systematization or theorification involves analytization.

(3) Not a relative increase in the stock of isolated synthetic

propositions (such as the so-called protocol sentences), but rather an increase in the percentage of analytic propositions, is a desideratum of scientific research, since this corresponds to a greater systematization or theorification. Scientific propositions, too, are status seekers.

The six previously listed advantages of the proposed redefinition of analyticity should be weighed against the last three consequences. If the latter were found undesirable, then the proposal should be rejected. The writer found them desirable because they match his image of science,[9] and this is why he invites you to ponder over the seemingly naive redefinition of 'analytic proposition' as the one which can be assigned a truth value upon rational examination—or analysis, for short.

Redefinitions do not win battles, but they may clarify and even stop quarrels about words, particularly about words so highly polymorphous (as Ryle would say) as 'analytic.' May the above redefinitions contribute to stop a dispute that has been instructive but that has lasted too long. More pressing tasks are waiting.

[9] See M. Bunge, *Metascientific Queries* (Springfield, Ill.: Charles Thomas, Publisher, 1959), especially Chapters 2 and 3.

# 3
# Levels

As used in contemporary science and ontology, the term 'level' is highly ambiguous. Most writers do not care to give a definition or even a distinct characterization of this word. As a result, one and the same name—'theory of levels'—is applied to a variety of doctrines having different referents. Thus, while the neo-Platonist has in mind links in the Chain of Being, the mechanist may refer just to degrees of complexity, and the biologist either to integrated wholes or to stages in evolution. No wonder that they should often misunderstand each other if they speak of different things while designating them with one and the same word.

The aim of the present chapter is to list the most usual, and some of the possible, meanings of the word 'level,' to characterize them briefly, to illustrate them, and to propose some philosophical problems in which those concepts are involved. Should this semantical clarification prove useful in clearing the ground for ontological speculation, the thesis would be confirmed that there is no conflict between semantics and ontology, as long as the former does not deny the legitimacy of inquiries into the referents of certain universal words, and as long as metaphysics is not resistent to logical hygiene.

Let us then proceed to examine the meanings of 'level' relevant to either science or philosophy.

## 1. *Level*$_1$ = *Degree*

In the context of ordinary knowledge levels are conceived as degrees or grades in a static scale, or as stages in a process. Different levels are not, in this sense, necessarily marked by differences in qualities; they may just be different intensities of the same property. An obvious symbolic representation of this concept is the graded ruler.

*Definition.* An object belongs to a degree $D_n$ higher than another degree, $D_{n-1}$, if and only if it surpasses in at least one respect all the objects belonging to the lower degree. (This definition breaks down for continuous degrees.)

*Peculiar relations:*

(1) $D_n = D'_{n-1}$ ($D_n$ is the follower of $D_{n-1}$ in a given sequence.)

(2) $D_n > D_{n-1}$ ($D_n$ is higher than $D_{n-1}$ in a certain respect.)

*Illustrations.* (1) Degrees of extensive quantities (e.g., height) or intensive ones (e.g., population density). (2) Degrees of integration, adaptation, learning, proficiency, originality, truth. (3) Degrees of importance in relation to some end.

*Queries.* (1) Why use the word 'level' instead of 'degree' when no qualitative changes are involved in the transition from one degree to another? 'Level' is, in fact, highly suggestive of qualitative difference. (2) What is the range of the hypothesis of continuity, according to which differences in degree can all be made as small as desired? (3) Does classification require discontinuity in some respect, or is it possible to classify according to the degree or intensity of continuous variables? Would the latter procedure not introduce an element of convention incompatible with the aim of natural classification?

## 2. *Level$_2$ = Degree of Complexity*

As conceived by mechanistic ontologies, levels are nothing but degrees in scales of complexity, to the exclusion of qualitative newness. In this sense, level$_2$ is a specification of level$_1$.

*Definition.* An object belongs to a degree of complexity $C_n$ higher than another, $C_{n-1}$, if and only if the number of its constituents, and consequently the number of its interrelations, is larger than both the number of elements and mutual relations of the objects belonging to the lower degree.

*Peculiar relations:*

Relations (1) and (2) of the preceding section, plus

(3) $\hat{x}\,(C_n x) > \hat{x}\,(C_{n-1} x)$ (The higher the degree of complexity, the more members it contains.)

*Illustrations.* (1) Simple machines—Complex machines. (2) Magnetic domain—Large scale magnet. (3) Comte's classification of the sciences.

*Queries.* (1) Is it worthwhile to define an absolute degree of complexity, or are there as many scales of complexity as respects (number, quality, relation, . . .) being investigated? (2) Is there a lowest level of complexity *in re*? (3) According to the above definition the water filling a bucket is more complex than the water contained in a droplet. Would it be possible to define a degree of *specific* complexity which made mere quantity irrelevant to it?

### 3. *Level$_3$ = Degree of Analytic Depth*

Most philosophers and scientists are prepared to grant the existence of levels of analysis, even if they do not all acknowledge that some of these levels of knowledge may correspond—certainly in a complex way—to levels of being. In this sense, level$_3$ is a specification of level$_1$.

*Definition.* A piece of knowledge (description, hypothesis, theory, technique, method) belongs to a degree of analysis $A_n$ deeper than another, $A_{n-1}$, if and only if it accounts for a larger number of features of the referents common to both pieces of knowledge, or if it explains some properties occurring in $A_{n-1}$ in terms of concepts peculiar to $A_n$, or if it decomposes its object more thoroughly than $A_{n-1}$ does, or if it reveals a finer mesh of relations.

*Peculiar relations:*

Relations (1) and (2) of section 1, plus

(4) $A_{n-1}\,(P \cup S) A_n$ (The lower level of analysis is part of [$P$] or is subsumed [or sublated] under [$S$] the higher level.)

*Illustrations.* (1) Geometrical optics—Young and Fresnel's mechanical wave optics—Electromagnetic theory of light—Quantum theory of radiation. (2) Thermodynamics—Statistical mechanics. (3) Propositional calculus—Predicate calculus.

*Queries.* (1) Granted that not all the levels of scientific and ontologic analysis disclose different levels of being,[1] why should some of the jumps in the degree of depth of analysis not correspond to objective levels—as happens, e.g., in the case of psychology in relation to neurophysiology? (2) What are the separate contributions of objective complexity in a given respect, and richness of conceptual outfit, to the degree of analytic depth? (3) Is there a maximum depth in the analysis of matters

[1] See M. Bunge, *Metascientific Queries* (Springfield, Ill.: Charles C. Thomas, Publisher, 1959), Chapter 5.

of fact, as there is a limit in the analysis of ideal objects (existence of primitive concepts and propositions)? In particular, is it true that Heisenberg's uncertainty relations establish a limitation upon empirical analysis?

## 4. *Level*$_4$ = *Emergent Whole*

A level, in this sense, is a concrete or ideal whole, a self-contained unit—such as a cell or a proposition—characterized by qualities of its own and, if complex and concrete, by a strong interaction of its parts. The lower order wholes are the building blocks of the higher order ones; the latter emerge through the harmonious mutual action (integration) of lower order individual units. In some cases the higher levels are the environment of the lower ones. This connotation of 'level' is frequent among biologists[2] and psychologists,[3] who often add to it the qualifier 'integrative,' or speak right away of 'levels of organization.' The concept was also used by N. Hartmann[4] in connection with the lowest (prepsychical) levels of reality. A picture of a level structure in this sense is a set of concentric spheres.

*Description.* An emergent whole is an entity that, in some respects, behaves as a unit; if complex, it is highly integrated and has qualities which its parts lack; and it arises from lower order units and may give rise to higher order emergent wholes.

[2] See, e.g., J. Needham, *Time: The Refreshing River* (London: Allen & Unwin, 1943), pp. 160 ff and 233 ff. A. B. Novikoff, "The Concept of Integrative Levels in Biology," *Science,* 101 (1945), 209.

[3] See, e.g., T. C. Schneirla, "Levels in the Psychological Capacities of Animals," in R. W. Sellars, V. J. McGill and M. Farber (Eds.), *Philosophy for the Future: The Quest of Modern Materialism* (New York: The Macmillan Co., 1949).

[4] N. Hartmann, *Philosophie der Natur* (Berlin: de Gruyter, 1950), Chapter 41. Emergent wholes are loosely called *Gefüge* (structures) by Hartmann.

*Peculiar relations:*
Relations (1) and (2) of section 1, Relation (3) of section 2, and

(5) $W_n\ (P \cap S)\ W_{n+1}$ (The lower emergent wholes are parts of [P] and are subsumed or sublated under [S] the higher on es.)

*Illustrations.* (1) "Elementary" particle—Atomic nucleus—Atom—Molecule—Brownian particle—Body—Celestial body—Star group—Galaxy—Galaxy cluster—Universe. (2) Aminoacid molecule—Protein molecule—Protein crystal—Cell—Metozoan organism—Social unit (forest, flock, community, etc.). (3) Concept—Proposition—Theory—Science.

*Queries.* (1) If the predicate 'integrative,' which derives from 'integration' (coordination of the parts, or harmonious interconnection) applies to complex objects rather than to grades in an evolutionary sequence, is not 'integrative level' advantageously replaced by 'emergent whole'? (2) Is the two-place predicate 'sublated under' inherently non-extensional, or is it merely a confused word? (3) Are there ultimately simple wholes (atoms of some sort) in the external world, or is rather wholeness or atomicity relative to the level of existence?

### 5. *Level$_5$ = Poistem*

By 'poistem' (from *poiótes,* quality, and *systema,* system) I mean a system or bundle of qualities, whether primary or secondary; that is, a group of interrelated properties without implication of intrinsic order within the system itself or in the sum total of systems. Quality groups or domains have been considered by Keynes[5]; bundles of sensible qualities have been dealt with by Russell.[6] A picture of a level structure is in this case a set of partially overlapping circles.

*Description.* A poistem is a system of interrelated qualities

[5] J. M. Keynes, *A Treatise on Probability* (London: Macmillan, 1921 and 1929), Chapter xxii.

[6] B. Russell, *An Inquiry into Meaning and Truth* (London: Allen & Unwin, 1940), Chapter vi.

or variables. Symbolically: the $n$-th poistem is the $n$-th set of qualities:

$$P_n = \{Q_i\}_n.$$

*Peculiar relations:*

(6) $(i)\,(\exists n)\; Q_i \in P_n$ (Every quality belongs to at least one poistem.)

(7) $(\exists i)\,(\exists k)\,(\exists R)\; Q_i R Q_k$ (Some qualities are related to each other.)

(8) $P_n \cdot P_{n+1} \neq 0$ (Contiguous poistems partially overlap.)

*Illustrations.* (1) Domain of mechanical phenomena—Field of life phenomena—Realm of historical events. (2) The state of a system (physical, biological, social, etc.) as specified by the set of values of a system of variables. (3) The intension or connotation of a concept is the system of predicates (the poistem) that characterize it.

*Queries.* (1) Do poistems have a factual counterpart, or are they arbitrary (or else subjective) categorizations, as diffusionism maintains with respect to cultural traits? In other words, are there natural kinds or is every class a logical fiction? (2) Are there non-overlapping poistems, i.e., counterexamples to relation (8) above? (3) Is there a finite number of poistems?

### 6. *Level$_6$ = Rank*

The term 'hierarchy' (system of hierarchical grades) is abusively used with a variety of meanings; often, when only linear order is meant. It is convenient to restrict it to sequences of terms ordered by a one-sided, i.e., asymmetric dependence relation. A picture of hierarchies is the staircase pyramid.

*Description.* A rank (or hierarchical grade, or grade in a hierarchy) is an element in a discrete linear sequence, such that its status (importance, power, or value) is higher or lower than the neighboring ranks, and such that, unless it is the highest of all, it is dependent in some respect on the higher ranks.

*Peculiar relations:*
Relation (1) of section 1, plus

(9) $R_n > R_{n+1}$ (The status of $R_n$ is higher than that of $R_{n+1}$.)

(10) $R_m \cdot R_n = 0, m \neq n$ (Different ranks have no common members.)

(11) $R_n \ dep \ R_{n-1}, n \neq 1$ (The lower ranks depend on the higher ones.)

(12) $\hat{x}(R_{n-1}x) < \hat{x}(R_n x)$ (The higher the rank, the less members it contains.)

*Illustrations.* (1) Institutional hierarchies. (2) Plotinus' chain of being: The One—Spirit—World-Soul—Earthly things—Matter. (3) Functions in living beings.

*Queries.* (1) Are hierarchies absolute, or is every gradation of ranks relative to one or more properties? (2) Are hierarchical orders everywhere not occasionally reversed? (3) Are there strict hierarchies in nature, or are there rather nets of interdependent entities, out of which approximate hierarchies can be isolated for limited spacetime regions? [7]

## 7. *Level$_7$ = Layer*

Levels are sometimes conceived as layers,[8] i.e., as superposed strata arranged according to the order of their emergence in time, or their logical precedence. A picture of level structures in this sense is a set of geological strata.

*Description.* A layer or stratum is a section of reality characterized by emergent qualities. Symbolically: $S_n = \{Q_n\}$, where '$Q_n$' designates one of the *nova* peculiar to $S_n$.

[7] The last two questions are discussed in M. Bunge, "On the Connections Among Levels," *Proceedings of the XIIth International Congress of Philosophy* (Firenze: Sansoni, 1960), VI, 63.

[8] E.g., N. Hartmann, *Neue Wege der Ontologie,* 3rd ed. (Stuttgart: Kohlhammer, 1949), especially Chapter v. The relation between the supra-organic layers ("soul" and "spirit") and the lower strata (matter and life) is regarded by Hartmann as one of superposition (*Überbauungsverhältnis*).

*Peculiar relations:*
Relation (1) of section 1, and

(13) $S_{n-1}$ *prec* $S_n$, where '*prec*' designates any relation of the class of relations of precedence (temporal, causal, logical, etc.).

(14) $S_m \cdot S_n = 0, m \neq n$ (Different strata have no common members.)

*Illustrations.* (1) Sense-data propositions—Empirical generalizations—Theoretical law-statements. (2) First-order functions (properties of individuals)—Second-order functions (properties of first-order properties)—Etc. (3) Singular propositions—Theorems—Axioms.

*Queries.* (1) Are the *nova* in each stratum altogether independent of the qualities of the lower strata as regards their subsistence, or are they free in limited respects only? (2) Are layer structures in material reality static, or do occasional reversals occur? (3) Are strata not exclusive of discourse, since apparently the higher grades both in nature and in culture are rooted in the lower ones and not simply superposed on them?

## 8. *Level*$_8$ = *Rooted Layer*

If the successive grades of being are regarded, not only as emergent upon one another in a linear way, but also as rooted in the lower levels and as retaining all the qualities that characterize the latter, then the concept of rooted level is involved. This concept can be found among biologists[9] (often intermingled with those of emergent whole and degree of complexity, whether *in re* or in analysis); it is also typical of emergentist philosophers.[10] A picture of a level structure in this sense is that of a telescopic system.

[9] E.g., O. T. Bailey, "Levels of Research in the Biological Sciences," *Philosophy of Science,* 12 (1945), 1.

[10] S. Alexander, *Space, Time, and Deity* (New York: The Humanities Press, 1920), II, pp. 46, 68, and *passim.* C. Lloyd Morgan, *The Emergence of Novelty* (London: Williams & Norgate, 1933), pp. 29, 41, and *passim.* R. W. Sellars, *Evolutionary Naturalism* (Chicago: Open Court Publishing Co., 1922).

*Definition.* An object belongs to a rooted layer $Y_n$, higher than another, $Y_{n-1}$, if and only if, in addition to all the qualities that characterize $Y_{n-1}$, it has a set of emergent qualities $Q_n$ of its own.

*Peculiar relations:*

Relation (1) of section 1, plus

(15) $Y_n \; em \; Y_{n-1}$, where '*em*' designates 'emerges from.'

(16) $Y_n = Y_{n-1} + \{Q_n\}$, where '$Q_n$' designates the *nova* of $Y_n$.

(17) $Y_m \cdot Y_n \neq 0$ (Superposition with common elements.)

*Illustrations.* (1) Levels of language: Object-language—Metalanguage—Etc. (2) Logic—Set theory—Arithmetics—Mathematical analysis. (3) Superposition of cultural patterns derived from cultural contacts (commerce, colonization, conquest, etc.)

*Queries.* (1) Is there a ground floor of being, i.e., a bottom level underlying every other grade of existence? (2) What is the relation of rooted layers to emergent wholes: are the latter simply the members of the former? (3) Are there rooted layers in the external world? (It would seem that the superposition of patterns occurs in the highest levels only, whereas the spontaneous emergence of qualities in nature is not cumulative, some qualities being lost in the process of emergence.)

## 9. *Level$_9$*

Levels in this sense are grades of being ordered, not in arbitrary ways, but in one or more evolutionary series. Although most authors conceive of the level structure of reality as a linear gradation, non-linear (parallel, branching, etc.) arrangements are conceivable; for example, the following scheme has been proposed for the main levels of reality:[11]

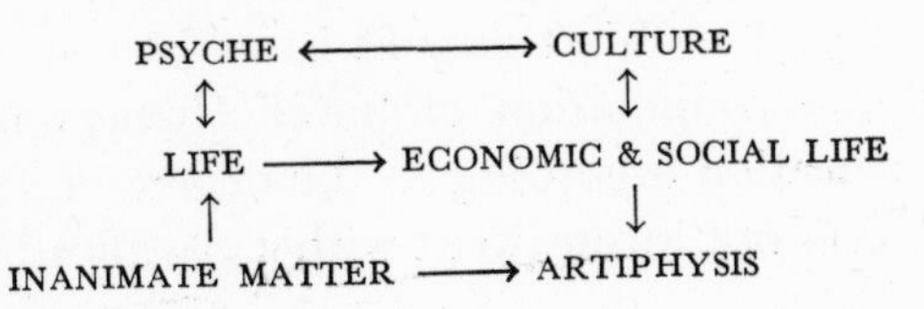


[11]M. Bunge, *op. cit.* (in fn. 7).

*Description.*[12] A level is a section of reality characterized by a set of interlocked properties and laws, some of which are thought to be peculiar to the given domain and to have emerged in time from other (lower or higher) levels existing previously.

*Peculiar relation:*

(18) $L_n \; em \; L_{n-1}$ ($L_n$ emerges from $L_{n-1}$.)

*Illustrations.* (1) Atomic phenomena—Chemical phenomena—Biological phenomena—Psychical phenomena. (2) Ganglia—Spinal Chord—Palaeoencephalon—Cerebral cortex. (3) Reality—Experience—Knowledge.

*Queries:* (1) What does 'higher than' mean in connection with $levels_9$? More complex, or qualitatively richer, or better organized—or all this taken together? (2) Could definite criteria be set up (*a*) to characterize the concept of emergence in an unambiguous and nonmystic way, and (*b*) for the splitting of levels into sublevels? (3) Could the mind-body problem be construed as the question of the mutual actions of bodily functions belonging to different levels?

## 10. *Concluding Remarks*

All of the nine meanings of 'level' examined above are or can be used in ontology, and a few more might perhaps be discerned and refined, notably the concept of degree of specific complexity. Since they are definitely different, no occasion for conflict should arise among ontological theories having different meanings of 'level' in mind. The only possible conflict is with experience: some level concepts may lack a real counterpart.

One and the same object may fit in various level structures, especially if the connotation of 'level' changes in each case. Thus, a classification according to the degree of complexity in a given respect is not inconsistent with a classification according

[12] M. Bunge, *op. cit.* (in fn. 1).

to the qualities involved; e.g., heavy atoms are not only more complex wholes than light atoms but belong also to different poistems and, moreover, their properties are determined by the number and kind of nuclear particles involved.

Of all the nine concepts, the last—which we have called plainly *level*—seems to be equivalent to what many biologists, psychologists, and social scientists[13] call *level of organization.* On the other hand, what scientists call *integrative level* is often identical with the kind of systems we have called *emergent whole.*

Notice that, according to the description given in the last section, (*a*) if the principle of limited variety[14] is rejected, there is no a priori limit to the division of levels of organization into sublevels; (*b*) every derivative level$_9$ is rooted in the parent levels (lower or higher) but need not retain all their qualities: the emergence of new characteristics may be accompanied by the loss of some properties; (*c*) the relation 'higher than' has in this context nothing to do with valuation; values may occur, on the other hand, in connection with hierarchies; (*d*) lower levels$_9$ may arise from higher ones, as is the case with parasitic organisms and artifacts; (*c*) events and processes at lower levels$_9$ may be produced by changes taking place at higher levels, as illustrated by the purposeful movements of the limbs; (*f*) the higher levels$_9$, in contrast with both emergent wholes and ranks, need not be less populated than the lower ones; e.g., there may be fewer thinking rushes than machines; (*g*) level structures are not static but dynamic; (*h*) one-way relations are not found among all levels$_9$.

Although all the nine concepts listed above seem to be used in contemporary science and ontology, the notion of level$_9$—or level, for short—seems to be particularly useful in the building of scientifically oriented ontologies and outlooks, since it affords a means for a realistic and unified categorization of

[13] E.g., J. H. Stewart, "Levels of Sociocultural Integration: An Operational Concept," *Southwestern Journal of Anthropology,* 7 (1951), 374.
[14] See J. M. Keynes, *op. cit.,* (in fn. 5), p. 258.

pieces of material and cultural reality, in a way reminiscent of natural and evolutionary classifications. Let us hope that such theories may yield an increasingly faithful and rich picture of the universe such that, to the extent to which it succeeds in combining diversity with unity, and in avoiding ontological reductionism (whether mechanistic or spiritualistic), it could be called *integrated pluralism*. Most concepts examined in this chapter might occur in such a picture.

# II

# SIMPLICITY AND TRUTH

# 4

# Logical Simplicity

To live is to face complexities, and the foremost rules for approaching the problems they raise are, perhaps, "Try the simplest course first" and "Simplify: Polish blurs and decompose the given problem into simpler tasks." The analysis of complexes into simples or, rather, into simpler units, is a desideratum in both practical and theoretical endeavors. But analysis itself may be a complex task, and instead of eliminating complexities it may disclose them. Moreover, simplicity is easier to preach than to define. Because, like 'analyticity' and 'level' and so many other key words, the term 'simplicity' covers a cluster of concepts.

Now, if simplicity is a complex concept—as we will attempt to show—then it is essential to disclose and distinguish its various dimensions before advising the choice of the simplest practical or theoretical course, and even before approaching problems such as those of establishing the relations of simplicity to testability and truth. That is to say, we should analyze 'simplicity' before using the term, unless we want it to remain vague to the point of meaninglessness.

## 1. *Ontological and Semiotic Simplicity*

Before analyzing the predicate 'simple' we should know to what it can be attributed. It seems clear that two kinds of objects can be ordered in respect of complexity (or simplicity): namely, material and cultural objects (things, events, processes) and their properties, on the one hand, and ideal objects (such as concepts, propositions, and theories) and their properties, on the other. Or, stated simply and rather inaccurately, two kinds of object can be simple: things and signs. We shall speak accordingly of *ontological simplicity* and of *semiotic simplicity*.

Ontological simplicity has been postulated—and challenged—from the most ancient times. Semiotic simplicity has been sought—and sometimes purposefully avoided—of old as well, by poets and scientists alike, although the theory of the simplicity of signs is still in its infancy. That nature and man are "basically" simple, is an ancient ontological tenet—more precisely, a heuristically valuable prejudice—that can be adequately examined on the basis of science alone, since we judge the simplicity (or the complexity) of reality through the simplicity of the scientific knowledge of it. Consequently, before approaching ontological simplicity we should examine the simplicity of signs, a semiotic problem that has only recently been faced in a scientific spirit.

Four dimensions of semiotic simplicity will be studied in this chapter and in the following: syntactical (or logical) simplicity, or economy of forms; semantical simplicity, or economy of presuppositions; epistemological simplicity, or economy of transcendent terms; and pragmatic simplicity, or economy of work. Logical or formal simplicity will be attacked in this chapter.

Now, there are basically four types of sign in the field of discourse: terms, propositions, proposals, and theories. Hence, we must successively study the simplicity of terms (designating concepts), sentences (expressing propositions and proposals), and theories (systems of propositions). In turn, since propositions and proposals are built out of predicates (like 'between'), names of extralogical constants (like 'Argentina') and variables (such as '$x$'), logical constants (e.g., 'or'), logical prefixes (like 'all'), and modal prefixes (such as 'possibly'), a methodical study of logical simplicity should begin by examining the formal complexity of predicates, leaving individual constants and variables aside, because they are essentially given by the subject matter, so that they cannot be varied at will. Now, if we assume that one and the same system of logic underlies all language systems occurring in rational discourse—which is true as a first approximation—we may leave out of account the complexity of logical signs, which constitute a constant background common to nearly all meaningful discourses. The logical complexity of *extralogical* predicates will accordingly be studied in the first place.[1]

## 2. *Logical Simplicity of Terms*

Predicates may be formally simple (e.g., 'extended') or complex (e.g., 'extended over a sphere'); i.e., atomic or molecular. Further, predicates may be one-placed (e.g., 'long') or many-placed (e.g., 'longer than'). They may also be of the first order (designating properties of individuals), such as 'hot,' or of a higher order (designating properties of properties), such as 're-

[1] This was the approach of A. Lindenbaum in his pioneering paper "Sur la simplicité formelle des notions," *Actes du Congrès International de Philosophie Scientifique* (Paris: Hermann, 1936), VII, 28.

lational property.' From a further point of view, predicates may be dichotomic (presence/absence predicates), like 'curved,' or metrical (designating quantitative properties), like 'curvature'; in the last case they are often called numerical functors.

Consequently, a rough measure of the complexity $C$ of a dichotomic (nonmetrical) predicate might be the sum of the number $A$ of its atomic constituents (degree of molecularity), the total number $P$ of places of the atomic predicates (i.e. their degrees), and their total order number $O$, i.e.,

$$C = A + P + O. \tag{1}$$

Thus, the complexity value of 'black' would be $C = 1 + 1 + 1 = 3$. Since this is the lowest value $C$ can have, it is convenient to normalize it to unity by dividing the complexity value by three. With this normalization the simplicity value $S$ of a predicate would be given by

$$S = \frac{1}{C} = \frac{3}{A + P + O} \tag{2}$$

This function ranges from 0 (infinite complexity) to 1 (minimum complexity).

Notice that the preceding estimate of $C$ presupposes the context of common-sense knowledge. In science 'black' is regarded as a derivative, hence molecular, predicate elucidated in some such way as this: "completely absorbing all electromagnetic wave-lengths." Further analyzed the definition becomes

$$\text{black } x =_{df} (y) \ [y \text{ is an electromagnetic wave-length} \rightarrow x \text{ absorbs } y \ \& \ (\text{absorption coefficient of } x = 1)]. \tag{3}$$

Three extralogical predicates, all of the first order $(O = 1)$ occur in the definiens of 'black' in the context of physics. The first is molecular with degree of molecularity $A = 2$, and the others are atomic $(A = 1)$; their degree or place numbers are 1, 2 and 1 respectively. Hence the complexity value of 'black' in physics would be 4 $(=$ total molecularity $= 2+1+1) + 4$ $(=$ total number of places $= 1+2+1) + 3$ $(=$ total order number $= 1 + 1 + 1) = 11$, which upon normalization yields

$C$('black'/Physics) $= 11/3$. The corresponding simplicity value is $3/11$, approximately one-fourth the value found for the same term in the context of ordinary language. The *complexity of predicates is, then, contextual.* Moreover, scientific analysis does not necessarily decrease but, on the contrary, is apt to increase the complexity of concepts. To require the simplification of concepts amounts to stopping analysis.

In the above elucidation of the predicate 'black' we have introduced two metrical predicates (numerical functors): 'electromagnetic wave-length' and 'absorption coefficient,' and we have rated them on a par with the nonmetrical dyadic relation 'absorbs.' However, metrical predicates, the most characteristic of modern science, are, so to say, "infinitely" more complex than nonmetrical ones, since they are associated with an infinite (and often continuous) set of numerical values. 'Black,' when meaningful at all, is either true or false of a given object, whereas the numerical variable 'wave-length' may take on an infinity of values. The measure represented by formula (2) above neglects this complexity of metrical predicates and must therefore be changed.

In order to account for the above-mentioned complexity of metrical predicates we might decide to measure this aspect of complexity by some function $f(v)$ of the number of values, $v$, that predicates may take on, and such that $f(2) = 1$ (for dichotomic or classificatory predicates), and $f(\infty) = V < \infty$ (for metrical predicates), $V$ being the same for all metrical predicates. Then the total complexity value of a term $t$ in a system $L$ (a given language system, or a given scientific theory) would be

(3) $$C(t/L) = \tfrac{1}{3}[\text{Total molecularity of } t \text{ in } L + \text{Total number of places of } t \text{ in } L + \text{Total order number of } t \text{ in } L + V(t/L)]$$
$$= \tfrac{1}{3}[A(t/L) + P(t/L) + O(t/L) + V(t/L)]$$

But the following objections suggest themselves immediately. In the first place some metrical predicates, like 'wave-length' or 'distance,' have an infinite range, whereas others, such as 'absorption coefficient' or 'velocity,' have a finite range (though, of course, an infinity of possible values). Why should we rate on a par predicates having so widely different ranges as 'distance' —which varies between 0 and $\infty$—and 'absorption coefficient,' which is bounded by 0 and 1? Secondly, there are infinitely many numbers $V$ and, moreover, infinitely many well-behaved functions $f(v)$ that fulfill the border conditions $f(2) = 1$ and $f(\infty) = V < \infty$ required above. Without further conditions any choice among the double infinity of upper bounds $V$ and functions $f(v)$ would be much too arbitrary. Thirdly, even if this indeterminacy could be removed with the addition of some reasonable postulate, there does not seem to be any reason why the four numbers, $A$, $P$, $O$ and $V$, which are manifestly inhomogeneous, should be added without further ado, particularly since the predicate order is so much weightier than, say, the number of places.

These difficulties may be among the reasons why the few logicians who have tried to set up measures of the complexity of predicates have not taken into consideration whether they are metrical or not. As a consequence their theories are not even applicable to present-day ordinary language, where more and more numerical functors occur. In fact, the laborious search for an adequate measure of the structural richness of sets of extralogical predicates is under way,[2] but up to now only very modest results have been obtained; they are significant in relation to pauper model languages in which the predicates are both nonmetrical and mutually independent—which is not the case of scientific sign systems.

Take, for instance, Kemeny's proposal [2] to measure the richness of the basic extralogical vocabulary (i.e., of the set of extralogical predicates that are taken as primitives in a theory) by a

[2]A. Lindenbaum, reference 1; N. Goodman, *The Structure of Appearance* (Cambridge, Mass.: Harvard University Press, 1951), Chapter III, "Axiomatic Measurement of Simplicity," *Journal of Philosophy,* 52 (1955), 709, and "The Test of Simplicity," *Science, 128,* 1064 (1958); J. G. Kemeny, "Two Measures of Complexity," *Journal of Philosophy,* 52 (1955), 722.

function of the number of models, or "linguistically possible worlds," of the set of predicates. Now, since a single continuous numerical functor, like 'position,' yields infinite "models" of that kind, Kemeny is forced to restrict his calculus of simplicity to classificatory and order predicates; and even for these dichotomic concepts he requires a finite domain of individuals—which is consistent with empiricist ontologies but totally at variance with the needs of science. A generalization of Kemeny's measure to cover infinite universes is not possible, so an approach not based on the number of "models" of a logical system should be sought. That the approach under examination is inadequate can also be seen from another angle.

The possible states attainable by the universe—or, if preferred, the possible state descriptions—are not determined by a set of independent predicates and, even less, by a set of non-metrical independent variables, but rather by the partially known set of all the *laws* of nature and society, which laws consist of definite relations among predicates which are very often metrical. If we want to know, say, what are the "possible worlds" that might be built with such a "simple" object as a single vibrating string, i.e., if we want to know what its possible modes of vibration are, we must solve the vibrating string equation (law) with definite boundary and initial conditions. And this is not a language problem; moreover, the solution physics obtains is useless for the approach under consideration, since the number of possible "models" (or state descriptions) of a vibrating string is infinite. State descriptions are of little interest in isolation from law statements.

Further complications ought to be accounted for. One of them is the possible mutual dependence of predicates by way of law statements. A second source of complexity not taken into account in the available theories of complexity stems from the interrelations of terms in any system worth this name. Even if isolated symbols could be assigned finite complexity values in an unambiguous way, the fact should be faced that there *are* no isolated symbols: every symbol belongs to some language system. Now, a symbol immersed in a language may be manifestly simple yet potentially complex, owing to the possible metamorphoses allowed by the transformation rules of the system. Thus the numeral '1' can be written as

$$m/n,\ -n/-n,\ i \cdot (-i),\ (-1)^{2n},\ a^0,\ \cos 0,\ \lim_{n \to \infty} a^{1/n}$$

and so on and so forth *ad infinitum.* In this sense every number sign is infinitely complex despite its manifest simplicity. Consequently, separate measures should be set up for *manifest complexity* and *latent complexity* when dealing with nonprimitive predicates. Also, measuring the complexity of primitives does not exhaust the problem unless the rules of transformation allowed by the system are extremely poor.

We conclude that the theory of the syntactical simplicity of terms is an inspiring yet underdeveloped enterprise, the results of which are so far inapplicable to the estimate of the complexity of propositions actually occurring in ordinary language, let alone in scientific languages. If the theory of simplicity is to be of any use, it must cease avoiding complexities in actual sign systems. The rule "Simplify" should not lead us to circumvent complexities by building ideally simple linguistic toys; theories of simplicity need not be simple themselves.

### 3. *Logical Simplicity of Sentences*

Let it first be said that the *logical,* not the *linguistic* simplicity of sentences will be investigated in the following. That the two are different is shown by the following example. "Science is interesting" is linguistically simpler than "Natural science is interesting and cultural science is interesting"; but since the two sentences are logically equivalent, they must be assigned the same logical complexity. In other words, linguistic brevity is consistent with logical complexity and vice versa.

Atomic propositions are obviously simpler than molecular ones, at the propositional level at least. It is tempting to measure the formal complexity of a proposition $p$ by assuming that the connectives eventually occurring in it are all equally simple—hence irrelevant to the complexity value—and by counting the number $N(p)$ of its logically independent (atomic) constituents, or by adding unity to the number of its connectives.[3] We should then have $C(p) = N(p)$, whence the simplicity of $p$ could be defined as $S(p) = 1/N(p)$. In particular,

$$C(p \,\&\, q) = C(p \vee q) = C(p) + C(q) = 2.$$

But this is too coarse a measure, for it neglects nothing less than the inner complexity of the atomic constituents themselves, which may contain complex predicates. A better measure would be the inverse of the sum ($\Sigma$) of the complexity values of the atomic propositions $p_i$ making up $p$, namely

$$S(p) = 1/\Sigma C(p_i). \tag{4}$$

But here we find again the unsolved difficulties mentioned in the previous section, notably the one regarding the measure of metrical predicates. And even if we decided to measure only propositional complexity, we would meet a grave obstacle posed by universal propositions. In effect, let '$(x)Fx$' be such a proposition. If the universe of reference consists of $n$ individuals, named $c_1, c_2, \ldots, c_n$, the complexity value of $(x)Fx$ will be that of $Fc_1 \,\&\, Fc_2 \,\&\, \ldots \,\&\, Fc_n$. Since the complexity of every one of these factors is the same, the complexity of the universal statement is

$$C[(x)Fx] = n \cdot C(Fc_i)$$

which tends to infinity as $n$ approaches infinity. According to formula (4), then, all strictly universal propositions have the same simplicity value—zero. This renders the proposed measure irrelevant to science.

[3] This is, essentially, the proposal of H. Kiesow, "Anwendung eines Einfachheitsprinzip auf die Wahrscheinlichkeitstheorie," *Archiv für Mathematische Logik und Grundlagenforschung,* 4 (1958), 27. See also H. Hermes, "Zum Einfachheitszprinzip in der Wahrscheinlichkeitsrechnung," *Dialectica,* 12 (1958), 317.

Wrinch and Jeffreys[4] have attempted to measure the complexity of a certain class of universal propositions containing metrical variables and only such predicates. They did not analyze the predicates themselves, and they restricted their treatment to physical laws expressible as differential equations, on the controvertible (but frequent) assumption that "Every law of physics is expressible as a differential equation of finite order and degree, with rational coefficients." Later on Jeffreys[5] proposed to restrict the coefficients to integers, defining the complexity of an equation of this kind as the sum of the order, the degree, and the absolute value of the coefficients. This proposal is open to the following objections.

In the first place, the degree of a differential equation is even more important than its order; thus a linear equation of the 2nd order is in every sense simpler than a first order and second degree equation (like Hamilton-Jacobi's). Secondly, the absolute value of the derivation order is not a faithful index of simplicity: a fourth order equation is not essentially more complex than a second order equation, whereas fractional order derivatives are enormously more complex than first order derivatives; thus, nobody would count a $\frac{1}{2}$-order differential equation as simpler than a first-order equation. Moreover, first-order (partial) differential equations are often more complex than second-order (partial) differential equations, this being the original reason for introducing potentials in Maxwell's theory. Thirdly, the numerical value of the coefficients is irrelevant: at most their ratio (not their sum) should count. Fourthly, the number of variables, on the other hand, is important, but it does not occur in the approach under consideration. Fifthly, a measure

[4] D. Wrinch and H. Jeffreys, "On Certain Fundamental Principles of Scientific Inquiry," *Philosophical Magazine,* 42 (1921), 369. Jeffreys abandoned this assumption in the 2nd ed. of his *Theory of Probability* (Oxford: Clarendon Press, 1948), p. 100. The pioneering work of Wrinch and Jeffreys has been practically overlooked.

[5] H. Jeffreys, *Scientific Inference,* 1st ed. (Cambridge: Cambridge University Press, 1931), p. 45.

of complexity obtained by adding entirely heterogeneous indices all equally rated looks suspiciously simple.

Another proposal is to measure the complexity of an equation, whether algebraic or differential, by the number of adjustable parameters in it.[6] But, again, this proposal overlooks the degree and the number of variables of an equation, as well as the fact that fractional derivation orders are more complex than integral ones. Compare the equation of light absorption,

$$u_x + \lambda u = 0$$

with the equation of light propagation,

$$u_{xx} + u_{yy} + u_{zz} - u_{tt} = 0.$$

If simplicity is to be equated with paucity of parameters, the second equation must be assigned the complexity value 0, and the former the value 1—but this is clearly wrong. Also, $y = x$ and $y = x^2$ are equally complex by the same token and, also, "because their consequences will usually differ so much that the discrimination between them by means of observation will be easy." [7] But this is certainly an undesirable procedure: the gauge of a logical property like syntactical complexity should not depend on empirical operations—and will be completely out of place if the signs happen to be devoid of empirical meaning.

It would seem that complexity has here been confused with generality and with derivativeness, as I will try to show by means of an example. The ellipse equation, $(x/a)^2 + (y/b)^2 = 1$, contains two adjustable parameters, $a$ and $b$. The hyperbola equation,

$$(x/a)^2 - (y/b)^2 = 1$$

has the same complexity value according to the criterion under examination, although we would rate the hyperbola roughly

[6] H. Jeffreys, *Theory of Probability,* 2nd ed. (Oxford: Clarendon Press, 1948), p. 100. K. R. Popper, *The Logic of Scientific Discovery,* 2nd ed. (London: Hutchinson, 1959), secs. 44-46 and *Appendix VIII.

[7] Jeffreys, *loc. cit.*

as twice as complex a curve as the ellipse, for having two branches. Again, the circle equation,

$$(x/a)^2 + (y/a)^2 = 1$$

contains the single parameter $a$, whence it would be half as complex as the ellipse or the hyperbola. However, a simple gauge transformation, namely,

$$x' = x/a, \quad y' = y/b,$$

leads from the ellipse to the circle, which shows that the former is *more general* than the latter ($b = a$ being a special case), but not necessarily more complex than it—or, if it is, then its complexity is not intrinsic but depends on the choice of the coordinate system, so that $C$ ought to be relativized to the latter.

In the second place, the more parameters a *physical* equation contains, the less *fundamental* it is, in so far as fundamentality can be defined as absence of numerical and material constants (in contrast with universal constants such as $c$, $e$, or $h$, and with mathematical constants such as $\pi$, which are characteristic of the mathematical tools employed). But fundamentality is an epistemological and ontological characteristic, not a logical one. Besides, fundamental equations are *methodologically* simpler than phenomenological relations, in that they are easier to dispose of, whereas the latter protect themselves against attempts at refutation by suitable adjustment of parameters. But, again, this can not be regarded as relevant to syntactical simplicity.

What is valuable in the proposal that the complexity of an expression of quantitative form be measured by the number of its adjustable parameters is the methodological aspect that has just been mentioned (ease of test), as well as an epistemological consequence of it, namely, that the larger the number of parameters an expression contains, the greater its probability will be—hence the less acceptable on any standpoint except phenomenalism and conventionalism, which anyhow are inimical to science, and inductivism, which is part of a naive philosophy of science.[8] But formal complexity should not be confused with difficulty of test, although the former may entail the latter. Besides, the identification of simplicity with paucity of parameters is powerless to gauge the complexity of propositions that cannot be given the form of an equation connecting metrical variables: it assigns the same complexity value (namely, 0) to all expressions in which no adjustable parameters occur, no matter how many atomic predicates they contain, and what their degree and order are.

We conclude that no adequate measure of the complexity of propositions is available.

## 4. *Logical Simplicity of Theories*

The complexity of systems of propositions must apparently depend on the number and complexity of their postulates—but how? No definite answer to this question can be given before a theory of the simplicity of propositions is available. However, a few remarks can be made.

In the first place, it is usually granted that the number of independent analyzed postulates of a theory is relevant to its complexity. Not, of course, the mere number of postulates—which by conjunction can always be reduced to one—but the number of statements containing no further independent statements, i.e., no further statements that might be regarded as postulates. But this is insufficient.

In the first place, one and the same body of knowledge may be organized and, particularly, axiomatized in many ways. In other words, one and the same theory may be *formulated* in various alternative ways, all of them equivalent, in the sense

[8] As is well known, the probability of statements increases with their vagueness and specificity, and decreases with their preciseness and generality. In particular, the probability of strictly universal statements is zero. The most convincing arguments against regarding high probability as a desideratum of scientific hypotheses have been given by K. R. Popper, *op. cit.* (in fn. 6), sec. 80 and *Appendix VII.

that exactly the same items of knowledge are interrelated. Some axiomatizations may contain a single postulate, others a large number, and this will only show that while some formulations of the theory have a simpler *basis* than other formulations, the overall complexity of the theory is not thereby altered: every simplification in the basis is paid for by a complication in the body of consequences.

In the second place, logically simple assumptions may have logically complex consequences, and equally $L$-simple assumptions may have consequences of unequal $L$-complexity. Thus, the hypothesis $dy/dx = ax$ leads, by integration, to $y = \frac{1}{2}\,ax^2 + b$, whereas the equally simple assumption $dy/dx = ay$ yields $y = b \exp(ax)$, which is obviously more complex than the former (being, in fact, a function not reducible to a polynomial, but expressible as an infinite series). As in the case of terms (see section 2), we have to distinguish the manifest from the latent complexity of a theory's postulates. The latent complexity of a theory's basis is given by the number and variety of its possible transformation, which is in turn determined by the number of its primitives and by the rules of transformation accepted by the theory. Unless we realize this, we will be tempted to assign all physical theories the same $L$-complexity value, since they can all be derived from a single variational principle each.

In short, *the logical simplicity of the basis of a theory does not warrant its overall formal simplicity*. That the complexity of transformation rules is more decisive than the number of primitives and postulates of a theory is clearly shown by mathematical analysis in comparison with arithmetic: both have the same basic vocabulary, but analysis is richer than arithmetic because its grammar is richer: it contains a larger number of operations. But how are we to measure the complexity of the rules of transformation regulating such operations? Their syntactical complexity, or even their theorematic power (the yield of theorems) will not do: the former does not say much about the complexity of the resulting system, and the latter may be infinite. What matters most is the degree of conceptual unity, or cohesiveness, the axioms and rules of transformation lead to, a cohesiveness to which definitions contribute as well.

## 5. *Conclusion*

The ultimate aim of the theory of logical simplicity should be to gauge the structural simplicity of theories. But there is no satisfactory, or even unsatisfactory, *L*-complexity measure of theories. We may well counsel the adoption of the rule "Choose the *L*-simplest among all the theories consistent with the available body of empirical evidence," but if we do not know how to gauge or at least how to compare degrees of *L*-complexity of theories, our advice will not be more effective than wishing good-night.

Besides, are we sure we *ought* to prefer the logically simplest among all the possible theories consistent with the known empirical data? The simplest of all factual "theories" would be just the conjunction of the given observational propositions in a given field, since there is only a finite number of them. But this would not be a *theory* proper, because nothing could be logically deduced from it; in particular, it would make neither explanation nor prediction possible.

To sum up, the theory of logical simplicity is an underdeveloped important project. It is underdeveloped because, owing to its inherent complexity, it has attracted too small a number of workers, and also because it has been approached in a simplistic manner; as a result, not a single satisfactory gauge of the structural simplicity of concepts, propositions, and theories is available. And the project is important not because it could help in propagating the cult of simplicity but because it would dispel the myth that "ideas cannot be counted" and because it would serve to estimate the degree of complexity—i.e., of richness and depth—of human knowledge notwithstanding the pessimism of philosophic Dadaism.

# 5

# Extralogical Simplicity

Most studies on simplicity deal only with the structural or logical dimension of the problem. We shall distinguish three further dimensions, still semiotic all of them: the semantical, the epistemological, and the pragmatic ones.

## 1. *Semantical Simplicity: Economy of Presuppositions*

### 1.1. *Semantical Simplicity of Terms*

This subject seems to be virgin: logicians have been predominantly interested in formal simplicity of simple languages and, as a consequence, they have rated as equivalent all concepts having the same logical form and type, e.g., 'one' and 'Socrates.' However, the complexity of meaning is at least as important as the complexity of form, although the latter must certainly be approached first, both because it is less elusive and because the meanings that can be assigned to a sign depend in part on its form. (Thus, a relation term cannot refer to a single individual.) A few informal remarks will be enough to show the richness of the subject.

There is a trivial sense in which a term '$t_1$' may be said to be semantically more complex than a second term '$t_2$'—namely, if '$t_1$' has a larger number of different acceptations than '$t_2$.' It is in this sense that 'simplicity,' 'level,' 'analyticity,' 'freedom,' and 'democracy' are said to be complex terms. We shall not be concerned with this kind of semantic complexity, because it is a linguistic problem. On the other hand, the body of assumptions and beliefs that "stands behind" any given concept does pose a genuine philosophical problem, to which we now turn.

That 'theory' denotes a concept more complex than 'proposition' does, although both are syntactically equally complex, will easily be conceded; the same happens with 'living' in relation to 'assimilating' and with 'electron' in relation to 'mass.' The reason for this unequal complexity seems to be this: 'proposition' occurs in the definiens of 'theory,' but normally not vice versa, and the same is true for the other examples.

The more complex term *presupposes* a larger number of concepts and propositions (e.g., laws of nature) than the simpler does. Or, if you prefer, the meaning of the more complex notions is specified (not necessarily in an explicit and unambiguous way) by a larger number of concepts and propositions than is the case with the simpler ones.[1] Thus, 'velocity' presupposes 'distance' and 'duration,' which may in turn be regarded as primitives in the context of present-day physics; whence we may say that 'velocity' is *semantically* more complex than either 'distance' or 'duration.' On the other hand, 'force' is as complex as 'mass' in the context of Newtonian mechanics.

[1] For an elucidation of the notion of specification of meaning, see A. Kaplan, "Definition and Specification of Meaning," *Journal of Philosophy,* 43 (1946), 281.

The remarks above suggest establishing the following measure of the simplicity of a concept from a semantical point of view. The *S*-simplicity of a term '*t*' (designating a concept) in the language system *L* (e.g., that of a theory) is the inverse of the number of its extralogical specifiers of meaning:

$$(1) \qquad S(t/L) = 1/M(t/L).$$

For example, in the arithmetic of natural numbers as formalized by Peano, 'one' and 'successor' are primitives, hence their *S*-complexity value is zero. On the other hand, since '2' $=_{df}$ 'successor of 1,' the complexity value of '2' is 2. Notice that, on the above stipulation, intensional or semantical simplicity is contextual. Choosing 0 as primitive instead of 1, the *S*-complexity value of '2' becomes 3.

However, various objections may be raised against the proposal above. Firstly, according to it the *S*-complexity value of the number 10,000 would be one thousand times larger than that of 10—and this looks counterintuitive. This shortcoming might be met by choosing some smoothing function of the number *M* of specifiers of meaning, such as log $M(t/L)$. With this choice we would have

$$C(10{,}000/\text{Peano arithmetic}) = \log_{10}(10^4) = 4,$$

whereas

$$C(10/\text{Peano arithmetic}) = \log_{10}(10^1) = 1,$$

which seems more satisfactory. But then the *S*-complexity value of 1 would no longer be zero, but

$$C(1) = \log_{10} 0 = -\infty$$

which is meaningless having presupposed that *C* should be a positive or at least zero number.

Of course, a different function might be chosen which would not yield an undesirable value for the beginner of the sequence of integers. For example, $C = \log(1 + M)$, $C = 1 - e^{-M}$, and $C = \text{Tanh}\, M$ would do. But why just *these* among the infinity of functions—for instance, $\log_a{}^n (1 + M)^n$, $\log_b (1 + M)^n$, Tanh

$M^{1/n}$, $1 - e^{-M^n}$, and so on—that might do the same job? The obvious rejoinder is, of course, that log $(1 + M)$, $1 - e^{-M}$ and Tanh $M$ are to be preferred because they are simpler and more familiar than most other functions with the same smoothing property. Yet, this appeal to simplicity does not reduce the ambiguity altogether and it employs an intuitive, presystematic notion of simplicity.

Besides, the specifiers of meaning cannot be counted accurately in nonformalized languages, which are by far the most numerous. Partly because the specification of meaning is in them circular or interconceptual rather than linear.[2] And partly because the disclosure of the ideas "behind" a given concept is both a historical and a logical task: terms denote concepts, concepts belong to views, theories, and conceptions, and the latter are part of intellectual culture, which is anything but a closed set.

An exhaustive conceptual analysis would have to take the whole cultural background into account, particularly as regards critical words like 'idea' or 'cause.' Even so, not all of the presuppositions would be dug out: (*a*) if the analysandum is familiar to us, because we should overlook precisely what is most obvious; (*b*) if it belongs to a past period, because we cannot reconstruct with arbitrary accuracy the ideas, attitudes, and desiderata of any past period. Counting presuppositions is an almost hopeless task. Consequently, *S*-simplicity could be measured in formalized languages alone—i.e., where it is hardly an interesting problem. Finally, even if the number of specifiers of meaning could be counted in interesting cases, there is no reason why they should all be assigned the same weight unless they all occurred as primitives in the given system.

In short, no reasonable way of measuring the *S*-simplicity of terms is in sight. Consequently for the time being we shall have to content ourselves with the qualitative concept of semantical complexity.

[2] See C. W. Churchman, "Concepts without Primitives," *Philosophy of Science,* 20 (1953), 257.

### 1.2. *Semantical Simplicity of Propositions*

Supposing we had a reasonable theory of the semantical simplicity of terms, we still would have to build a theory of the simplicity of propositions with respect to meaning. We might, of course, try something like the reciprocal of the sum of the *S*-complexity values of the extralogical predicates occurring in the proposition. But it does not seem likely that such complexity values are summable unless the predicates are independent —which, again, is an unrealistic assumption in the case of science, which might be described as a quest for interconnection.

A simpler, and probably more fertile, approach would be to count the number of presuppositions a proposition has in a given context. Take, for instance, the rival cosmological hypotheses "The universe exists from all eternity," and "The universe has had a beginning in time." The former is *S*-simpler than the latter, in the sense that it does not require any of an unlimited number of hypotheses about the alleged creation mechanism. A comparative, not a quantitative *S*-simplicity concept is thereby suggested, because only in formalized theories is it possible to count ideas accurately.

### 1.3. *Semantical Simplicity of Theories*

There is an urgent need for the treatment of this problem, because scientists actually apply (mostly in a tacit way) criteria of evaluation and selection of theories with respect to their semantical complexity. Thus physicists dislike complicated mathematics in so far as it obstructs the interpretation of their formulas in physical terms: they make every effort to simplify the initial and the final mathematics because syntactically complex expressions are difficult to "read" in terms of properties, events, and processes. They do not mind too much if the intermediary computations are lengthy or even clumsy—although they care for expediency and elegance as much as the mathematicians do—on condition that both the postulates and their testable consequences are semantically simple. (Because, as

Fresnel said, nature does not worry about our analytical difficulties; and because, as experience teaches, graduate students can always be found to do the boring computations.) The comparative semantical simplicity of both the postulates and the testable consequents of general relativity is one of the reasons for its acceptance despite its notorious epistemological and pragmatic (particularly, psychological and algorithmic) complexity.

But how are we to gauge the semantical complexity of theories if we barely know how to estimate that of propositions? The most we can state at the moment is the truism that the semantical complexity of theories is determined by both the formal and the semantical complexity of their postulates and rules of transformation and designation. But this is both too obvious and too vague. It shows that, if the theory of logical simplicity is an infant, that of semantical simplicity is not yet born. A good opportunity for semanticists.

## 2. *Epistemological Simplicity: Economy of Transcendent Terms*

Let us call epistemological simplicity the closeness to sense experience and, in particular, to observation. The degree of epistemological complexity (or abstractness) is, then, a sort of "distance" from sense experience, a kind of measure of the gap between constructs and percepts. If preferred, epistemological simplicity can be called degree of ostensiveness, or fewness of transcendent or transempirical concepts[3]—terms which, like 'conductivity,' 'randomness,' 'violence,' and 'love,' have no referents that can be pointed to and no sense-data they can be reduced to.

Phenomenalistic utterances—like "I feel a white patch"—are the simplest with regard to epistemological simplicity. (But,

[3] This is the kind of simplicity dealt with by J. O. Wisdom in *Foundations of Inference in Natural Science* (London: Methuen, 1952), Chapter vii.

as was pointed out in Chapter 4, section 2, phenomenal predicates are, in the context of scientific theory, syntactically more complex than physical ones, hence also semantically more complex, this being one of the reasons for not using them as primitives.) Then come, in order of epistemological complexity, ordinary physicalist expressions—like "This is chalk"—and finally, in the same order, scientific physicalist sentences, like "This is a sample of calcium carbonate." Predominantly phenomenalist languages—to the extent to which they are possible—achieve epistemological simplicity, or triviality, at the cost of both syntactical complexity and epistemological shallowness: it takes longer to say less in phenomenalist languages. The latter are not economical, but just poor.

A famous instance of epistemological simplicism is Mach's attempt to construe physical objects as complexes of sensations, a proposal later on refined by Russell. At one time, Russell [4] declared that the "supreme maxim in scientific philosophizing" is this: "Wherever possible, logical constructions are to be substituted for inferred entities." The aim of this "logical construction" was to *reduce* all concepts to the least hypothetical elements, to the most secure data, which were declared to be sense-data. Thus, the thing of common-sense was defined as the class of its appearances. "A complete application of the method which substitutes constructions for inferences would exhibit matter wholly in terms of sense-data, and even, we may add, of the sense-data of a single person, since the sense-data of others cannot be known without some elements of inference." [5] The desire for epistemological economy—based in turn on the yearnings for certainty—leads, then, to an attempt to "establish physics upon a solipsistic basis." [6] As is well known, Russell subsequently abandoned this programme, which was inimical to the objectivity and depth of science.

[4] B. Russell, "The Relation of Sense-Data to Physics" (1914). Reprinted in *Mysticism and Logic* (London: Pelican, 1953), p. 148.

[5] Russell, *op. cit.*, p. 150.

[6] Russell, *ibid.*

Syntactical economy and epistemological depth are won by introducing constructs,[7] that is, by increasing the epistemological complexity of theories. One of the most important results of recent epistemology is Craig's demonstration[8] that it is possible to dispense with all the transcendent or diaphenomenal terms of a theory, by building another "theory" containing observable predicates only—but at the price of giving up a finite postulational basis in favor of an infinite one. In other terms, once a theory has been built it is possible to destroy its rich superstructure and, by using its debris only, to build a huge one-floor store of observational data: the new "theory's" postulates will be the infinite conjunctions of the lowest-level theorems derived from the original theory. In short, epistemological economy is possible, but it must be performed *a posteriori:* it does not save theoretical work, since it requires a genuine theory first and then a pseudotheory. Besides, such an epistemological economy must be paid for by a loss of insight and by an infinite syntactical complexity.

Predominantly physicalist languages, in which theoretical constructs occur, such as 'electric charge' and 'surplus value,' allow for a greater logical cohesiveness and compactness, a deeper understanding, and an easier refutability (they take more risks than phenomenalist constructions, which ultimately inform only about our subjective feelings). Besides, physical-object languages enable us to distinguish the subject from the object, appearance from reality, the finite known from the infinite unknown, and so on; finally, they render communication possible (a strictly phenomenalist language would be private), and they are interesting.

Modern science did not discourage phenomenalist philosophers but it has definitely involved the downfall of phenome-

[7] The essential role of constructs has been emphasized by H. Margenau, *The Nature of Physical Reality* (New York: McGraw-Hill Book Co., 1950), Chapters 4 and 5.

[8] W. Craig, "Replacement of Auxiliary Expressions," *Philosophical Review,* 65 (1956), 38.

nalism within the field of science; since the 17th century scientists have not striven for epistemological simplicity but, on the contrary, have been inventing more and more transcendent (transempirical) concepts, more and more theoretical entities, with the sole restrictions that they be part of theories, scrutable (not necessarily observable), and fertile. It suffices to recall the atomic analysis of phenomenally continuous bodies, the replacement of the gravitational pull by a higher-order observable like space-time curvature, and the introduction of the psi-function, that bewildering source of both observables and unobservables.[9]

Physicists do not choose secondary or sensible qualities as fundamental variables; on the contrary, fundamental physical variables (like position and time) and fundamental physical parameters (like mass and charge) are not reducible to sense perception: they are constructs and it is not possible to construe them as "logical constructions" in the sense once advocated by Russell. Not even phenomenological (or black box) theories comply with the dictates of phenomenalism.[10] A further aspect of the departure from immediate experience—hence another source of epistemological complication—is the enrichment of the set of relations among constructs, namely, the system of definitions and law statements. In short, *the progress of science is accompanied by epistemological complication.*

However, science does not strive for epistemological luxury either: it does not seek epistemological complexity for its own sake, it does not multiply transempirical entities without necessity. A high order of mediacy (a low degree of epistemological simplicity) is not established out of servility toward some system of transcendental metaphysics—as was the case with medieval science—but is forced upon us by (*a*) the desiderata

[9] For an examination of physical terms lacking material and/or empirical correlates, see M. Bunge, *Metascientific Queries* (Springfield, Ill.: Charles C. Thomas, Publisher, 1959), pp. 252 ff.

[10] See my "Phenomenological Theories," in M. Bunge (ed.), *The Critical Approach* (Glencoe, Ill.: The Free Press, 1963).

of moderate formal, semantical, and pragmatic simplicity, and (*b*) the complexity of reality, which is intelligible but not sensible in its entirety. At least, the invention of constructs more and more distant from sense experience would be incomprehensible if reality were simple, and if we were not under the pressure of coping with its complexity by organizing our conceptual outfit around a set of highly fertile basic constructs.

The invention of scientific constructs is subject to some rules which prevent their *useless* multiplication. Firstly, every construct, however high its order of mediacy (remoteness from sense-data), must somehow somewhere be related, by means of correspondence rules (e.g., coordinative definitions) and law statements, to lower-order concepts. Secondly, constructs must ultimately be incorporated in testable theories. (Terms such as 'superego' and 'telepathy' are not objected to because they are transempirical but because they do not occur in testable theories.) Thirdly, conceptual entities should not be multiplied *in vain* (Occam's razor); but they should be welcomed whenever they lead either to a deeper understanding of reality or to a syntactical simplification of theories. In this respect, science seems to take a middle course between the poverty of phenomenalism and the waste of transcendentalism.

What was said above refers primarily to the epistemological simplicity of terms; but much the same applies to the epistemological simplicity of propositions and theories. *Unnecessarily* complicated assumptions and theories should be avoided: hypotheses and theoretical systems employing inscrutable predicates, such as 'Providence' and 'collective unconscious,' should be shaven with Occam's razor. Notice, however, that the latter does not hang in the air but falls under the more general rule, "Do not propose ungrounded and untestable hypotheses." (See Chapter 7.)

Furthermore, a complication of initially simple assumptions may well be unavoidable in the face of an increasing incompatibility with the body of empirical evidence. We should encourage such an increase in epistemological complexity if it does not consist merely in adding arbitrarily adjustable parameters (frequent among phenomenological theories) or untestable *ad hoc* hypotheses, but involves, rather, an enrichment of our picture of the world, e.g., an increase in its accuracy. Thus, to a first approximation, the acceleration of gravity can be regarded as independent of height and of the earth radius; but as soon as we wish to compute the orbit of an artificial satellite we need a more exact formula, which contains both the height and the earth radius—scrutable predicates to which we unambiguously assign objective properties—and this is never the case with the adjustable parameters that plague phenomenological theories.

All this, even if it were true, is too sketchy. One should attempt to find at least an ordering relation among concepts of different degrees of epistemological complexity; one should try to elucidate such intuitively acceptable orderings as e.g., "quantity of heat—temperature—energy—entropy" (an order which is not determined by physical theory). But a point may be reached where epistemological and psychological simplicity become indistinguishable: one cannot help imagining that, if our remote descendants were endowed with a sensory apparatus finer than our own, they would employ scientific constructs which we would regard as entirely unintuitive.[11] This leads us to the last class of simplicity to be distinguished here.

## 3. *Pragmatic Simplicity: Economy of Work*

From a pragmatic viewpoint, sign complexes can be arranged in respect to simplicity of at least the following kinds.

### 3.1. *Psychological Simplicity*

Psychological simplicity consists in obviousness, ease of understanding, or familiarity. Thus, Ptolemy's postulate that the

[11] For the historical relativity of intuitability, see M. Bunge, *Intuition and Science* (Englewood Cliffs, N. J.: Prentice-Hall, Inc., 1962), Chapter 3.

earth is stationary is psychologically and epistemologically simpler than the heliocentric hypothesis, and psychoanalysis requires far less previous training than psychology does, although it is epistemologically more complex than psychology on account of the number of inscrutable predicates it contains. The psychological complexity $C(x,y)$ of an object, problem, or procedure $x$, for a subject (animal or person) $y$, might be measured by the time needed by $y$ to "apprehend" the object, or to solve the problem, or to master the procedure. In maze problems, where trial and error is at work, $C$ might be measured by the proportion of unsuccessful trials.

An alternative measure of psychological complexity, proposed by Birkhoff,[12] is the sum of the efforts or tensions of the various automatic adjustments occurring in the subject during the "apprehension" of the object. This proposal is tempting because it involves a psychological model, but it poses the difficult problem of objectifying the tensions, and it is obviously inadequate in relation with nonautomatic behavior.

This is the type of simplicity that seems to be envisaged by the partisans of the economy of thought and particularly by Mach,[13] who described scientific research as a business (*Geschäft*) pursued for the sake of saving thought. Psychological simplicity is desirable both for practical (e.g., didactic and heuristic purposes: if preliminary theoretical models are to be set up, details must be brushed aside and easily understandable notions ("intuitive" ideas) must be seized upon. The obvious must be tried first, if only to dispose of it early: this is a well-known rule of intellectual work.

However, it should be borne in mind that (*a*) psychological simplicity is culturally and educationally conditioned, i.e., is not an intrinsic property of sign systems; (*b*) the deliberate neglect of a given factor should always be justified; (*c*) we must

[12] G. D. Birkhoff, *Aesthetic Measure* (Cambridge, Mass.: Harvard University Press, 1933).

[13] E. Mach, "Die Gestalten der Flüssigkeiten" (1868), in *Populär-wissenschaftliche Vorlesungen,* 4th ed. (Leipzig: Barth, 1910), p. 16.

be prepared to sacrifice psychological economy to depth and accuracy whenever the former becomes insufficient. For, whatever science is, it certainly is not a *business* whose concern is to save experience with the minimum expenditure of work.

### 3.2. *Notational Simplicity*

Notational simplicity consists in the economy and suggestive power of symbols. Thus the symbol '$P(h/e)$' for the probability of the hypothesis $h$ on the evidence $e$ is suggestive, hence easy to retain. And the vector and tensor representations are notationally simpler than the corresponding "analytical" (expanded) mode of writing. (Yet the vector and tensor calculus are not adopted because of their notational simplicity alone, but because they enable us to build and recognize quantities independent of the mode of representation, i.e., invariants with respect to coordinate transformations.)

Needless to say, compactness facilitates interpretations and favors retention, and well-chosen symbols may be heuristically valuable. Notational clumsiness and bulkiness, on the other hand, are obstacles to symbol manipulation and interpretation and, consequently, to thought—as must have been felt by the Greek mathematicians in connection with their system of numerical notation. Yet, compactness must not be exaggerated, as it often is in general relativity with detriment to clarity. Compactness is of little use if achieved through a long chain of nominal definitions, for then notational economy disguises semantical complication.

### 3.3. *Algorithmic Simplicity*

Algorithmic simplicity, or ease of computation, is something like the reciprocal of the number of steps in logical or mathematical calculation. (This number is actually estimated in the programming of computers.) Algorithmic simplicity depends on logical, semantical, and psychological simplicity, though not in a simple way. Thus the relation '$y < x$' is semantically simpler than '$y = x$,' in the sense that the equality relation is defined in terms of the two inequality relations. But the corresponding point set $\hat{x}\ \hat{y}\ (y < x)$ is algorithmically more complex than $\hat{x}\ \hat{y}\ (y = x)$, because finding the boundary of the former set presupposes determining the latter set.

Algorithmic simplicity is sometimes accomplished through complication of the basis; thus certain infinite series can best be computed by approximating them by integrals, and certain integrals of real functions become easier to compute if the real variable is replaced by a complex argument. Conversely, theories that are comparatively simple at their bases may be algorithmically complex; thus Dirac's theory of the electron, which starts with a notationally simple equation, requires such lengthy and difficult calculations that it is hardly used in computing electron behavior in accelerators, although there is no doubt about its comparative accuracy and depth.

A desideratum of science is to invent an algorithm—a "mechanical" decision procedure—for every class of problems. However, such thoughtless procedures, while pragmatically valuable, may not replace alternative, more complex operations, but may supplement them because the simpler procedures may save time at the price of giving up some insight.

### 3.4. *Experimental Simplicity*

Experimental simplicity is simplicity in the design, performance, and interpretation of observations and experiments. Hypotheses having the operationally simplest consequents, however complex they may be in all remaining respects, will be preferred by experimentalists. But this reasonable preference may have the undesirable consequence of delaying the empirical test of valuable complex theories. Therefore, experimental simplicity is not an absolute desideratum.

### 3.5. *Technical Simplicity*

Technical simplicity consists in easiness of application to practical, noncognitive goals. In applied science, where standards of tolerance are often large, and expediency and low cost may count more than accuracy, rough but simple theories are often preferred to more refined and complex ones. But considerations of technical simplicity should never brake the development of pure science.

## 4. *Which Simplicities Are Desirable, Why, and to What Extent?*

Various kinds of semiotic simplicity have been distinguished in this chapter and in the foregoing: syntactical, semantical, epistemological, and pragmatic economy. We do not know for certain how to measure every kind of complexity nor, indeed, whether they are all measurable. Even if we knew this, we still would have to find a suitable function of the various measures that might serve as an index for over-all complexity. Metaphorically we may say that complexity is a four-dimensional manifold in which it would be meaningless to define a distance (corresponding to the over-all degree of complexity), owing to the heterogeneity of the various dimensions.

Yet, although we lack an exact and complete theory of the simplicity of sign systems, we do possess some half-baked notions on the subject. This semi-intuitive (insufficiently analyzed) conception of simplicity may suffice for approaching the most interesting problems concerning its use, namely: *What kinds* of simplicity do we seek and to what extent? And *why* do we seek simplicity in some cases while avoiding it in others?

We want *syntactical simplicity* because it favors (*a*) systemicity or cohesiveness (exact formulation and conceptual connectedness being further factors of systemicity); (*b*) easy checking of consistency and/or completeness of the postulate basis, and (*c*) empirical testability (accuracy and scrutability being two further factors). In turn, we require systemicity and testability to the extent to which we want science.

Now, it is often asserted that logical simplicity is *decisive* in the choice among competing hypotheses and theories. But this is not true: as we shall see in Chapter 7, other criteria, such as accuracy and depth—which are manifestly incompatible with simplicity—are far weightier. Even formal criteria, such as symmetry and extensibility, may predominate over simplicity. Thus, when working in relativity physics, we would trust an assumption or a theorem of the form '$A_4B_i$' less than the formula $A_4B_i - A_iB_4$: the latter is more complex but is also more symmetrical and consequently capable of extension (namely, to the hexavector $A_\mu B_\nu - A_\nu B_\mu$). In this case, symmetry involves extensibility and is preferable to simplicity.

As to *semantical simplicity* or economy of presuppositions, we value it because, although we want systemicity, we also wish to be able to start research into new subjects without having to know everything else, and because it facilitates interpretation. There must be interconnections among the various fields of research and these must be compatible with one another, but such ties must allow for some play if the enterprise of knowing is to be possible at all.

Yet, it should be realized that semantical simplicity may be incompatible with syntactical economy, as shown by the following examples. (1) Mathematical transformations are comparatively simple in special relativity and in thermodynamics, but the physical interpretation of the formulas is often difficult; suffice it to recall the clock paradox and irreversibility. (2) Syntactical simplifications of physical formulas can be achieved by adopting certain systems of units (e.g., the so-called natural units $c = h = 1$) or by making certain changes of variables (e.g., by introducing $t = \cos \theta$). But such procedures, expedient as they are for purposes of computation, becloud the interpretation of the final results, since dimensional and geometrical considerations are among the main clues for the meaning of complex expressions occurring in physical theory.

With regard to *epistemological simplicity* (economy of transcendent concepts), we definitely do not want poverty of transcendent notions but seek rather a middle course between poverty and waste, and this because we wish to attain the richest and most accurate possible picture of reality with the help of the fewest indirectly testable assumptions. The motto of science is not just *Pauca* but rather *Plurima ex paucissimis*—the most out of the least. In short, we wish economy and not merely parsimony.[14]

Finally, *pragmatic simplicity* or economy of work is prized on quite different grounds: because we are limited, short-lived, hungry, lazy, stingy, impatient, and ambitious. One should not be ashamed of recognizing that the norm of pragmatic simplicity does not rank much higher than the counsel "Take it easy." While in many cases both are reasonable rules of conduct, there are occasions on which it is inconvenient or even immoral to choose the widest door. Sticking to pragmatic simplicity at all costs is making a virtue out of an imperfection and may lead—has led—to a serious damage to knowledge. Granted, useless toil should be avoided; but economy of work should not imperil universality and depth.

Scientists do not regard their work as a problem of minimization, but just the opposite; in particular, they know that simplification itself is not always a simple task but may require great labors and ingenuity. Moreover, they are aware that syntactical and pragmatic simplicity are to some extent mutually *incompatible* desiderata, because paucity in the basis will be overcompensated by lengthy developments, such as chains of definitions and computations.[15] For example, the binary base, which operates with the number signs '0' and '1,' is both logically-simplest and the semantically-simplest, to such an extent that human computers find it inconvenient; on the other hand, automatic computers are endowed with it (or, rather,

[14] See E. Cassirer, *Determinismus und Indeterminismus in der modernen Physik* (Göteborg: Elanders, 1937), p. 88.

[15] See W. V. Quine, *From a Logical Point of View* (Cambridge, Mass.: Harvard University Press, 1953), p. 26. That there might be a contradiction between syntactical and practical simplicity was denied, e.g., by Lindenbaum, in *op. cit.,* fn. 1, Chapter 4.

with its material counterpart) because simplicity of the basis is essential for artifacts, whereas the number of operations is comparatively irrelevant in them owing to their high speed.

Likewise, scientists and technicians are aware that semantical and epistemological simplicity are consistent with pragmatic complexity. Thus, the test or the application of a comparatively simple idea may be exasperatingly difficult, particularly in the sciences and technologies of man; reciprocally, other things are easier done than described and analyzed.

One might think that *conservation,* rather than minimization of mental energy, is at work in scientific matters—in the sense that an increase in complexity of a given kind tends to be compensated by a simplification of a different sort and vice versa.

### 5. *Conclusion*

In short, 'simplicity' is a multivocal term; not all kinds of simplicity are desirable or even compatible with one another; and the theory of simplicity, though still in a very rudimentary stage, threatens to become highly complex. Moreover, the search for a single measure of over-all complexity does not seem to make much sense owing to the different nature of the various kinds of complexity. This is not a declaration of skepticism, but a warning against one-sidednes and superficiality. If we wish to advance the subject we must face the complexity of 'simplicity' instead of seeking refuge in model languages that are simple by construction. No oversimplification of 'simplicity' will replace its analysis.

It would be difficult to conclude with any definite moral about the value of the various competing kinds of simplicity. One thing at least is certain, however; viz., that the simple injunction "Simplify" is inadequate, if only because it is ambiguous. If some rule has to be proposed, let it be the following: "Simplify in some respect as long as simplification does not eliminate interesting problems and does not carry a severe loss of generality, testability, or depth." This maxim is no less ambiguous, but at least it is less harmful than unqualified simplicism, which leads to forgetting that the goal of research is not to restrict itself but to attain truth.

# 6

# Simplicity and Truth

In this chapter and in the next we shall study the role of simplicities in science. Since scientific research begins with finding problems and culminates with weighing systems of hypotheses (theories), we shall have to watch the performance of simplicity along the path leading from meaningful question domains (problem clusters) to articulate answers (theories). In the present chapter we shall attain the core of science—hypothesis—and shall inquire into the relation of simplicity to truth, the ultimate goal of research; the relevance of simplicity to theory construction and assessment shall be investigated in the next chapter. But before doing this, the roots of simplicism should be dug up; otherwise we may not understand the vigor of the belief that simplicity plays a decisive role in science.

## 1. *Roots of Simplicism*

As it so often happens with philosophical tenets—and the Myth of Simplicity is certainly one of them—the motives behind the cult of simplicity fall into three categories: the legitimate, the ambiguous, and the illegitimate ones.

A first legitimate rationale of simplicism is the wish to disclose the primary units of discourse, the conceptual atoms in every field of thought—atoms which, of course, are simpler than the bodies of knowledge they constitute. This drive is legitimate because it is coincident with that of analysis, the chief aim of which is clarification. A second rationale, also of a logical nature, is the desire to increase the cohesiveness or systemicity of discourse: the fewer the initial concepts and premises, the more numerous will have to be the links among them in order to get a system;[1] this, too, is a legitimate motive because systemicity is a basic trait of scientific knowledge.

An ambiguous rationale of simplicism is the wish to understand, which is satisfied if the subject is impoverished. This motive is suspect because psychological simplicity is a subjective matter and because it may finish by demanding the sacrifice of deep truths, which too often are psychologically complex. A further ambivalent motive of simplicism is testability: up to a certain point this motive is reasonable, since simplicity of both the hypothesis to be checked and the checking procedure facilitate the former's test. On the other hand, the simpler hypotheses may also be the most simple-minded, and the simpler methods the least exact and exacting.

A definitely undesirable rationale sustaining the cult of simplicity is of a metaphysical nature: namely, the wish to attain the ultimate atoms of experience and/or reality (e.g., the "atomic facts"). This drive, which feeds metaphysical fundamentalism,

[1] N. Goodman, in *The Structure of Appearance* (Cambridge, Mass.: Harvard University Press, 1951), Chapter iii, has argued most persuasively in favor of this thesis.

is dangerous because it leads to postulating the final simplicity of some form of experience or some kind of substance, thereby barring any inquiry into their structure.

A further undesirable root of simplicism is infallibilism,[2] the doctrine summarized in the slogan "Safety first." It is true that "you diminish the risk of error with every diminution of entities and premises"; thus "if you can get on without assuming the metaphysical and constant desk in addition to the phenomenal desk, i.e., the set of its sensible appearances to you, you have a smaller risk of error than you had before. . . . That is the advantage of Occam's Razor, that it diminishes your risk of error." [3] But what is the use of security if it involves ignorance?

Of course, the assumption that there are physical objects somehow corresponding to my perceptions *is* risky. But without assuming this and many other hypotheses there is no science. (Besides, the assumption that my perceptions are never caused by external objects is even more risky—and barren.) Epistemological simplicism, the injunction to eschew the unfamiliar and abstract in order to diminish the danger of error, is an invitation to remain ignorant. "Safety first," a good slogan for driving, is lethal to the venturesome spirit of scientific research. The possibility of obtaining new and deeper and more accurate knowledge is drastically cut down by the allied requirements of simplicism, fundamentalism, and infallibilism. In science, just as in everyday life, "Nothing venture, nothing win," as Pauli once said.[4]

So much for the disclosure of the philosophical motives behind the cult of simplicity. (Obvious nonphilosophical motives are the practical and the aesthetic ones, which are beyond

[2] For a criticism of infallibilism and fundamentalism, see M. Bunge, *Intuition and Science* (Englewood Cliffs, N. J.: Prentice-Hall, Inc., 1962), Chapter 1.

[3] B. Russell, "The Philosophy of Logical Atomism," Lecture VIII, *The Monist*, 29 (1919), 378-9.

[4] W. Pauli, quoted by C. S. Wu, "The Neutrino," in M. Fierz and V. F. Weisskopf (Eds.), *Theoretical Physics in the Twentieth Century* (New York and London: Interscience, 1960), p. 251.

our domain.) Let us now study the actual functions of the various simplicities in scientific research.

## 2. *Simplicity in Problem Finding, Stating, and Solving*

It should be clear that simplicities are *un*desirable at the stage of problem finding, since the mere discovery or invention of problems adds to the existing complexity of life. The easy-going fellow, whether in daily life or in science, will abide by the maxim "Do not problematize," which is to say "Do not complicate things." In this way he will neither discover nor invent nor criticize anything.

Interesting problems are often found by applying this rule: *Complicate.* A complication introduced in a well-understood situation may generate a fruitful problem. Most generalizations involve complications, and the attempt to generalize is at the root of scientific thought. If, in a given body of formulas, we replace real coefficients by complex ones, linear terms by non-linear ones, homogeneous equations by nonhomogeneous ones, scalars by vectors, vectors by tensors, and so on, we effect so many nontrivial (noninductive) generalizations involving qualitative leaps. The resultant body of formulas will become more complex, i.e., richer, and some of the corresponding problems, such as finding the required new algorithms, or the true physical interpretations of the new, richer expressions, may be rewarding. (On the other hand, inductive generalization proper leads from a set of singular propositions, such as '$Fc_1$,' '$Fc_2$,' . . . , '$Fc_n$,' to a single compact expression of the form '$(x)Fx$,' which is at least linguistically simpler than the initial set. But this is not the kind of generalization involved in the extension of problems, theorems, and law statements.)

Research usually begins with pre-existent or with artificially produced messes rather than with clear-cut situations. And the organization of a mess into an understandable whole need not involve simplifications, although it often does involve them; such an organization frequently requires the invention of additional entities and operations. Simplification is sufficient for unification, but it is not necessary to this end and should be minimized in view of the important goals of accuracy, scope, and depth. We always start with complexities and never wish to end up in trivialities. A good rule for going beyond the known is: "Complicate the given, once it is fairly well understood, and see what happens. If some interesting and promising new idea arises in the treatment of the more complex problem, try to simplify the whole without losing the newness gained through the complication."

The injunction *Simplify!*, absurd as it is in the stage of problem finding, is most often indispensable when the time is ripe to formulate or *state* the problem in a clear and tractable manner. After all, we wish to solve our problems, and to this end we usually have but a few clumsy methods, so that we will try to simplify the given task in order to make it soluble at all, even if only an approximate solution can be secured.

But simplification or schematization of problem statements is done with a *practical* aim, not because it takes us nearer the truth: it does take us nearer the *solution,* but this will be the solution of a problem differing from the given problem, which may be more complex. Besides, simplification in one respect is often achieved through complication in another; thus the formulation and solution of problems involving spherical symmetry is simplified by employing spherical coordinates instead of rectangular coordinates, which are simpler.

The statement of a problem can be simplified in either of the following senses: (*a*) *without loss,* as when a biquadratic equation is reduced to a quadratic equation by means of the substitution $y = x^2$; (*b*) *with gain,* as when a statement about mental occurrences is translated into a set of physiological statements that can be put to the test; (*c*) *with loss,* as when heating is neglected in collision problems. The advantages of the former two simplifications are obvious; the status of the third kind of simplification, conspicuous in factual science and applied mathematics, is not realized by simplicism.

Most if not all formulations of scientific problems involve loss of complexity, i.e., involve some approximation consisting in the neglect of a number of factors occurring in the original problem. The given problem, too complex because it refers to a rich real situation, is transformed into a simpler question involving a schematization, hence an impoverishment relative to the actual situation. Without such simplifications no research could start. But, even though simplifications may involve ingenuity and even boldness, we are not too proud of them because they estrange us from reality. The simplification involved in problem statement is a means rather than an end: it is a means for making approximate solutions possible. Once the simpler problem has been solved, the more complex one can be approached and a closer contact with reality may thereby be gained.

Now, when a simplification is performed in the statement of a problem, the hypothesis is made that the approximation that has been made will be sufficient for the purpose in mind, or that the error resulting from the given simplification will be compensated by errors of another kind. Such methodological assumptions must, however, be checked; simplicity, a guarantee of solvability, is never a guarantee of truth. But the relation of simplicity to hypothesis deserves a separate treatment.

### 3. *Simplicity and the Testability of Hypotheses*

The simplest hypothesis is usually the first we hit upon and the first we send to the battle line of criticism and experience —and is also, as a rule, the first casualty. Dalton made the hypothesis that the simplest chemical composition is the most likely; in particular, he assumed that compounds of two substances were all diatomic. This belief in the favorable relevance of simplicity to truth led him to propose for water a formula we would now write $HO$, in contrast with $H_2O$, which we now believe to be the correct formula. Dalton's adherence to the tenet of simplicism caused a lot of confusion in chemistry during half a century—the more so because it was intermingled with a theory that was basically correct. Of course, the mistake did not lie in abiding by the methodological rule *Try the simplest first,* but in taking simplicity for a symptom of truth and in forgetting that progress, whether in science or elsewhere, involves complication alongside unification.

If the simplest and safest hypotheses were always to be preferred, classificatory statements should be made instead of comparative statements, and inequalities should be valued over equalities (e.g., equations). Yet in science one prefers an equality, such as '$x = a$,' or '$f(x) = 0$,' to the corresponding inequalities. The reasons for this preference must be stated precisely because we take the preference for granted. These reasons are:

(*a*) Equalities are more *exact* than inequalities: the latter have ambiguous solutions (think of the multiplicity of solutions of '$x > a$'); equalities, if solvable, have on the other hand exact solutions, though not necessarily unique and known.

(*b*) Equalities are better *testable* than inequalities. An inequality, such as '$x > a$' in the universe of real numbers, has a potential infinity of both confirming and refuting cases, whence it is as easy to confirm as to refute: its a priori testability is then very low. On the other hand, the corresponding equality, '$x = a$,' has a single confirming case and an infinity of refuting cases (namely, the set $\{x | x \neq a\}$); it is, consequently, easier to dispose of and, by Popper's criterion of refutability, it is preferable to more secure but less precise hypotheses.

Complex hypotheses are not difficult to illustrate or confirm, especially if they are framed either with a view to escaping refutation or in order to account for a body of empirical evidence *ad hoc* and *ex post facto;* in either case their degree of testability is small, either because they are shielded by further assumptions of the theory, or because they contain many conveniently adjustable parameters. This leads us to the problem of the so-called inductive simplicity,[5] which arises in the prob-

[5] H. Reichenbach, "Ziele und Wege der physikalischen Erkenntnis," in H. Geiger and K. Scheel (Eds.), *Handbuch der Physik* (Berlin: Springer, 1926 ff), IV (1929), p. 34.

lem of formulating a general hypothesis consistent with a number of empirical data, as is the case with curve-fitting.

Suppose we are given a set of $n$ empirical data consisting of $n$ pairs of numbers; every pair of numbers can be geometrically represented as a point on a coordinate plane. The problem is to trace a single curve passing through all the given points—i.e., to formulate a generalization subsuming the data at hand. Now, since an infinity of curves are compatible with the same set of data, the question is to choose among such an infinity of alternatives. Consider any two such curves, each representing a universal generalization from a finite body of empirical evidence; call them $H_1$ and $H_2$. Suppose hypothesis $H_1$ is syntactically simpler than hypothesis $H_2$; this comparative complexity of $H_2$ will roughly be reflected in the figure: the curve representing this hypothesis will be more wavy and irregular than the one representing $H_1$. Now, there is no limit to the possible complexity of $H_2$: a curve can be made to pass through as many points on the plane as desired—in fact, it can be made to cover an entire finite region, as is the case with Peano's famous curve. The empiricist is at a loss in the face of such a choice; since he will regard both $H_1$ and $H_2$ as "inductions" from the empirical data at hand, he will have to add a *nonempirical* stipulation, a convention, in order to make the choice. He will usually recommend the choice of "the simplest hypothesis compatible with the observed values." [6] By so doing he will renounce both empiricism and rationalism, since he will fail to provide a *ground* for this rule, which will then remain an arbitrary ukase.

The scientist, on the other hand, will proceed in the following way. He will first make sure whether the hypothesis to be chosen has to be contiguous with some body of knowledge or is, for the time being, an isolated hypothesis summarizing a set of empirical data. If the latter is the case, he will choose the simplest hypothesis, $H_1$. He will do this on a definite methodological

[6] For a careful statement and defence of this thesis, see J. G. Kemeny, "The Use of Simplicity in Induction," *Philosophical Review,* 62 (1953), 391.

ground: by sufficiently complicating the hypothesis $H_2$ it will become *irrefutable,* even though it will remain strictly *confirmed* by the available information if the curve $H_2$ passes through all of them. No new experimental datum could conceivably refute $H_2$ if it were to come very close to any given point on the plane. In short, we prefer in this case the simpler hypothesis because it is easier to refute.

But such a simplicity will not be taken as definitive: the scientist will be ready to complicate $H_1$ as soon as new data or new theoretical knowledge require it. Moreover, very simple hypotheses—such as straight lines—look suspicious, for experience has shown us that simplicity is not so much a property of reality as a property of our approach to reality: straight lines are usually first approximations, often averages over complex structures.

## 4. *The Role of Theory*

It is only when we are given to choose between a simple *isolated* (extratheoretical) hypothesis that nearly fits the observation, and a complex but equally *isolated* hypothesis giving an exact fit (as obtained by mechanically applying some method of interpolation), that we choose the former.[7] The ground of this policy of "inductive" simplicity is, in addition to convenience, again the fact that the simpler hypotheses are the easiest to eliminate.

The procedure will be different if the curve, far from representing an isolated hypothesis, is to meet the requirement of systemicity or theorification, i.e., of incorporation in some body of theory. In this case—never treated by inductivists and simplicists—the scientist will not choose the simplest hypothesis but rather *the hypothesis compatible with both the data at hand and the relevant theory,* without caring whether the chosen

[7] This point was stressed by D. Wrinch and H. Jeffreys, "On Certain Fundamental Principles of Scientific Inquiry," *Philosophical Magazine,* 42 (1921), 369.

assumption is the simplest compatible with either the data or the theory. He will even be prepared to sacrifice accuracy to theorification or systemicity, at least as long as the discrepancy between the accepted hypothesis and the empirical data is not much larger than the experimental error. A couple of examples will show why systemicity weighs more than simplicity in the evaluation of scientific hypotheses.

A set of points on a plane, suggesting a monotonously growing value of some variable, can be fitted by an infinity of algebraic functions, i.e., by polynomials of the form

$$y = a_n x^n + a_{n-1} x^{n-1} + \cdots + a_1 x + a_0;$$

normally a polynomial can be chosen that contains as many parameters (coefficients) as observations. But if a transcendental function like $y = b\exp(ax)$ or $y = b\mathrm{Ch}\ ax$ *nearly* fits the empirical evidence, it will be preferred to any simple polynomial because its theorification and, consequently, its rational test, will be easier: we know then what the elementary law is (namely, $y' - ay = 0$ in the first case, and $y'' - a^2 y = 0$ in the second case). And knowing this law we can set up a model—in this case a growth mechanism—accounting for the phenomenon in question. Notice that both the exponential and the hyperbolic function are infinitely more complex than any algebraic function: their series expansions contain each an infinity of coefficients.

Another example. Suppose the empirical dots suggest a wavy line. This can be fitted by an infinity of algebraic functions, but if a transcendental function like $\sin kx$ *nearly* fits the empirical evidence, then its theorification will be easier: its differential equation (which is perhaps the equation of motion) is $y'' + k^2 y = 0$, which in turn suggests the presence of an oscillatory mechanism. Polynomials, which are the only functions occurring in the inductivist treatments of the problem of formulating and selecting empirical hypotheses, play a small role in theoretical science just because, being too simple, they cannot hold the whole richness of reality. (Only infinite families of polynomials, such as, e.g., the spherical harmonics, are theoretically interesting, both because they are infinite and because they constitute systems. Isolated polynomials serve only the purpose of information packaging.)

It is consequently false that, as the inductivist and simplicist rule has it, "We ultimately prefer the simplest hypothesis compatible with the available empirical information." We normally prefer the hypothesis, whether simple or complex, compatible with (*a*) the available empirical evidence *and* (*b*) the bulk of knowledge *and* (*c*) the period's metascientific principles and tenets. It is only when dealing with *isolated* conjectures, i.e., in the absence of full-fledged theories, that simplicity is decisive, both for practical reasons and because simplicity is often favorable to testability. Whenever we are faced with alternative hypotheses that are equally backed by the empirical evidence, systemicity or connectedness will prevail.[8]

Now, testability depends not only on the hypothesis to be tested but also on the test technique. Therefore a word should be said about the relevance of the complexity of procedures of testing to the very possibility of testing. There is no doubt that methodological simplicity is a desideratum of science; to standardize procedures (e.g., to set up algorithms) for solving every possible set of well-stated problems, and to contrive "mechanical" procedures for checking the proposed solutions, is practically convenient. Yet the complexity of hypotheses will usually call for complex methods, and the increasing requirements of accuracy has the same effect of complicating test techniques.

Moreover, "mechanical" or thoughtless solution and checking procedures, while practically valuable, may not replace alternative, more involved procedures which, precisely by requiring more ingenuity, may go deeper in the matter. Thus the method of analytic geometry for solving problems in metrical geometry has not obliterated the old synthetic (nonalgebraic) method, because the latter provides in many cases a deeper insight than

[8] See P. Duhem, *La théorie physique,* 2nd ed. (Paris: Rivière, 1914), p. 259.

the former. Much in the same way, computers will continue supplementing pencil and paper operations without eliminating them: after all, somebody has to understand, plan, and control what is going on. Moreover, the design of accurate and high-speed methods involves complex theories and techniques. The final achievement of economy of work is always a result of intense work and creative imagination.

To sum up: *simplicity is ambiguously relevant to testability.* In some cases simplicity is favorable, in others unfavorable to testability. It is only when superficially restricting scientific inference to curve fitting and when the requirements of compatibility with scientific theory and metatheory are forgotten, that simplicity appears as an absolutely desirable characteristic. The fact is that empirical generalizations, if retained, are finally absorbed and corrected by theories, so that their support of simplicism, if any, is ephemeral. Science is not interested in simplicity by itself, but only in so far as simplicity may constitute a means for forming and checking our opinions. The ultimate goal of scientific research is not simplicity but truth.

## 5. *Simplicity and Truth*

Truth, if simple in some respect, is *easy to recognize and to check.* From this psychological and methodological fact the philosophical belief has been drawn that simplicity is a factor and a test of truth.[9] This belief is wrong and misleading. The mere fact that error, too, is recognizable on condition that it is not too complex, should suffice to dispose of the doctrine that truth and simplicity go hand and hand.

Scientists know that the richer truths are the more complex. Yet every one of us feels joy in the simplification of messy situa-

[9] See, e.g., N. Goodman, "The Test of Simplicity," *Science,* 128 (1958), 1064: "in the choice among alternative systems, truth and simplicity are not always clearly distinguishable factors. More often, simplicity is one test of truth." S. F. Barker, *Induction and Hypothesis* (Ithaca, N. Y.: Cornell University Press, 1957), p. 161: "Other things being equal, it is the simpler hypothesis which ought to be regarded as the better confirmed."

tions and in the building of systems simple in some respect. This does not prove that simplicity is a symptom of truth: an aesthetic feeling, and the finding of a transformation that renders problems more tractable are not signs of a semantic property but signs that work may start or stop. The illusion does not last long; even the most beautiful theory dealing with a section of reality is mercilessly subjected to exacting tests, until it is shown to be inadequate precisely for being *too simple,* e.g., for neglecting too many variables. No matter what philosophers may say, simplicity is never regarded by scientists as a *test* of truth, even though scientists with a faith in the ultimate simplicity of reality have occasionally regarded simplicity as a *symptom* of truth, and although conventionalists have gone as far as *defining* truth in terms of simplicity.

Those who maintain that the simplest is the truest, or at any rate the better confirmed, seem to forget that classical mechanics is in every respect simpler than either relativistic or quantum mechanics. They further seem to confuse the a priori likelihood of a hypothesis or of a theory, as gauged by means of metascientific criteria, with its a posteriori degree of corroboration. The simplest among a set of isolated hypotheses will be preferable, other things (empirical evidence) being equal, because of its greater practical convenience and its greater degree of refutability. (See sections 3 and 4 above.) But this does not establish the likelihood of the hypothesis, let alone its degree of corroboration. The degree of corroboration of a hypothesis is always assigned a posteriori, once its performance has been watched, i.e. once its compatibility with empirical data, theories, and metatheories has been established. The wish to secure hypotheses by a priori and conventional criteria, like maximum simplicity of some kind (which kind is seldom specified), is both antiscientific and at variance with any sound empiricism.

The history of knowledge, which is an epic of greater and greater approximation of truth, is not a process of mere simplification: for how could the initial naught be further simplified? Nor is it a process of unchecked complication: for how could we cope with it? Progress, in every domain, works through an increase in complexity; in particular, the truer hypotheses are usually more complex, at least in some sense, than the less true ones. But progress, whether of knowledge or of anything else, is not just complication but rather a synthesis of two opposite trends: one of complication and another of integration.[10] Integration, conceived as coordination, organization, or systematization, emerges just as a way of coping with increasing complexity; it unifies, at a higher level, what is disparate at lower levels. However, integration does not suppress complexity; it gives it, so to say, a structure or cohesion. This cohesion is achieved in science by theory. Let us then inquire into the relevance of simplicities to scientific theory.

[10] See M. Bunge, *Causality: The Place of the Causal Principle in Modern Science* (Cambridge, Mass.: Harvard University Press, 1959), pp. 290-291.

# 7

# Simplicity in Theory Construction

Any number of testable systems can be devised to cope with a given set of empirical data. The question is to hit on the *truest* theory—a scientific problem—and to *recognize the signs* of approximate truth—a metascientific problem. For, indeed, truth is not the unveiling of what had been occult: truth is made, not found, and to diagnose truth is as hard as to diagnose virtue. We have a working theory of the *complete* (not the approximate) truth of sentences,[1] but we have no satisfactory theory of the *approximate* truth of *theories* (systems of propositions) applicable to factual science.[2]

[1] A. Tarski, "The Semantic Conception of Truth," *Philosophy and Phenomenological Research,* 4 (1944), 341.

[2] An attempt to build such a theory is presented in Chapter 8.

To say that a factual or empirical theory is true if and only if its observable consequences are all true is inadequate on three counts. First, the theory may contain untestable assumptions and yet be consistent with observable facts; this is the case of all quantum theories. Second, there is no means of exhaustively testing the infinity of consequences (theorems) of quantitative scientific theories. Third, the notion of approximate truth is involved in factual theories. We should know by now that all factual theories are, strictly speaking, false: that they are more or less approximately true. A less simplistic and more realistic approach is therefore called for.

No decision procedure for recognizing the approximate truth of factual theories is available, but there are *symptoms* of truth, and the expert employs these signs in the evaluation of theories, as well as in their construction. Let us review these symptoms of truth and find out what simplicities are relevant to them, and in what manner.

## 1. *Assaying Criteria*

The construction and evaluation of scientific theories is guided, in a more or less obscure way, by a set of metascientific criteria which aim at maximizing the degree of truth. At least five groups of assaying criteria can be distinguished; they may be called syntactical, semantical, epistemological, methodological, and philosophical. Only a hurried view of these heuristic hints and testing criteria can be given here.[3]

### 1.1. *Syntactical Requirements*

(*a*) *Syntactical Correctness:* the propositions of the theory must be well formed and mutually consistent. Simplicity facilitates the *test* of syntactical correctness but is not a factor of it.

(*b*) *Systemicity:* scientific theories are systems, not just heaps,

[3] A more detailed study is made in M. Bunge, "The Weight of Simplicity in the Construction and Assaying of Scientific Theories," *Philosophy of Science*, 28 (1961), 120.

of corrigible propositions (hypotheses). Systemicity can be achieved by shrinking the number of basic concepts. But the simplification of the predicate basis of factual theories, in contradistinction with mathematical theories, has a limit which is rooted to the real net of properties. Thus, e.g., the four space-time coordinates are not interdefinable, and physics keeps adding fundamental, irreducible (but interconnected) properties. Conceptual connectedness, or sharing of basic concepts among the postulates of the theory, is a more important trait of scientific theory than economy of basic concepts. The concepts of a theory must, as it were, hang together if the theory is to be a conceptual whole and if it is to face the trial of experience as such, i.e., as a system. In short, formal simplicity, if possible at all, is sufficient but not necessary to ensure systemicity.

### 1.2. *Semantical Requirements*

(*a*) *Linguistic Exactness:* if the theory is to be empirically meaningful and unequivocally applicable, its ambiguity, vagueness, and obscurity must be minimal To this end it must avoid foggy terms such as 'small' and 'libido.' But the elimination of such undesirables has little to do with simplicity. Clarification is more often accompanied by complication—e.g., in the form of mathematical formulation—or, at least, by showing an actual complexity underneath an apparent simplicity. Hence, simplicity is unfavorably relevant to linguistic exactness, or at most irrelevant to it.

(*b*) *Empirical interpretability:* the theory must be applicable to specific situations. Simplicity is clearly unfavorable to this desideratum, since an abstract theory (a syntactical system) is simpler than an interpreted one (a semantical system). In connection with factual theories with an empirical import (i.e., with consequences that can be contrasted with empirical evidence), simplicity is, in the best of cases, irrelevant.

(*c*) *Representativeness:* it is desirable, but not mandatory, that the theory, far from being a merely predicting device, be representational or nonphenomenological. Theories accounting for the "mechanism" of events and processes afford a deeper understanding, take greater risks, and are more fertile than phenomenological theories.[4] Now, a strict adherence to the rules of logical and epistemological simplicity would require us to dispense with representational theories, since these usually involve not only the predicates of the related phenomenological systems, if any, but further, more abstract predicates of their own (e.g., 'molecule' in addition to 'temperature,' in the case of statistical thermodynamics as compared with phenomenological thermodynamics). Were we to follow the advice of simplicism, we would have to drop all the deeper theories of contemporary science, retaining only the black box theories.

(*d*) *Semantical simplicity:* it is convenient, for practical reasons, to economize presuppositions, since this will render the understanding, the test, and the application of the theory easier. But extreme semantical simplicity involves either fundamentality or lack of contacts with contiguous disciplines, i.e., weak external consistency or compatibility with the remaining body of knowledge.

### 1.3. *Epistemological Requirements*

(*a*) *External consistency:* the theory must be compatible with and, if possible, contiguous to, the bulk of accepted knowledge. This is not only a requirement of logical consistency but has also a methodological import: a theory contiguous to other theories has the latters' support. Now, simplicity is clearly unfavorable to external consistency, since the latter imposes a growing multiplicity of connections among the various chapters of science.

(*b*) *Explanatory power* = *Range* × *Accuracy:* the greater the range of the theory, the less properties will be involved; but the greater the accuracy, the more complex the theory will be. (See Chapter 6, section 3.) Consequently the demand for simplicity is ambiguously relevant to the demand for a large explanatory power.

[4] See fn. 10 in Chapter 5.

(*c*) *Predictive power* = (*Range explainable ex post facto* + *Unexpected range*) × *Accuracy:* simplicity is ambiguously favorable to predictability not only because it is incompatible with accuracy and compatible with manifest range, but also because the unexpected range of a theory (its serendipity) is greater as the theory is richer.

(*d*) *Depth:* it is desirable, though not necessary, that the theory involve essentials. But this requires epistemological sophistication, not simplicity.

(*e*) *Extensibility* or possibility of growth to cover new domains. It is desirable that the theory, far from being exhausted by the known empirical information, can be further worked out to cover new problems and, if possible, entire new domains. The capacity for linking or unifying hitherto unrelated domains is related to both external consistency and serendipity (predictability of unexpected effects). Hence simplicity, which is unfavorably relevant to these characteristics, is also unfavorably relevant to extensibility.

(*f*) *Fertility:* the theory must be a tool for further exploration, not simply a summary of past experience. This job can be done by false theories dealing with challenging problems. Obviously, simplicity is either irrelevant or unfavorably relevant to fruitfulness, since the latter will be related to range and depth.

(*g*) *Originality* or newness relative to precedent or rival systems: newness is desirable (yet neither mandatory nor always desired) not only as an intellectual stimulant, but also because it is a sign that previously ignored traits of the world have been uncovered. Now, the rules of simplicity obviously prohibit or at least discourage the framing of new, bold, constructs: the trite path is usually the simplest. This is particularly so in the case where theories are available which have been empirically confirmed, but which are unsatisfactory for some reason, e.g., because they are phenomenological. The policy of simplicism will in this case disavow new approaches and will thereby stop the advancement of science.

1.4. *Methodological Requirements*

(*a*) *Scrutability:* both the predicates and the methodological presuppositions of the theory must be scrutable; i.e., the theory must have testable consequences and its tests must be testable, that is, it must be possible to check them with further tests. A theory containing a large number of scrutable predicates will be preferable to another theory containing fewer predicates all or part of which are inscrutable, if only because the former theory will be testable, and the latter not. The *methodological* status of the predicate basis is, then, far more important than its logical structure and number. Thus 'electrically neutral' is both syntactically and semantically more complex than 'providential,' yet it is scrutable and may consequently occur in scientific theory, whereas the latter cannot. Yet an excessive logical complexity may obstruct scrutability, in the sense that logical derivations may be so difficult that testable consequences are hardly obtainable. In any case, simplicity is ambiguously relevant to scrutability, and criteria of scrutability of predicates are far from simple and uncontrovertible, as shown by the polemics around the "observables" of the quantum theory.

(*b*) *Refutability:* if the theory stands whatever the empirical evidence may be (as is the case of psychoanalysis), it cannot claim to be empirical. Clearly, semantical, epistemological, and experimental simplicity are favorable to refutability. But syntactical simplicity is ambiguously relevant to it: on the one hand, refutability requires accuracy, which in turn involves complexity; on the other hand, the fewer the predicates involved, and the simpler the relations assumed to hold among them, the easier it will be to refute the theory. But surely we do not wish actual refutation, which is immediately obtained by over-simplification; and facts, insensible as they are to our labors, may stubbornly refuse to lend themselves to logical simplification. Forced simplification will lead to actual refutation rather than just securing testability.

(*c*) *Confirmability:* favorable instances of the most remote consequences of the theory's basic assumptions must in principle be possible. Now, a theory can be complicated ex profeso in order to increase its degree of confirmation; hence, simplicity is unfavorably relevant to confirmation.

(*d*) *Methodological simplicity:* it must be technically possible to test the theory with reasonable accuracy and within a reasonable period of time. Much too complex experiments are inconclusive, because they involve many sources of error and many auxiliary assumptions. But no deep theory should be dismissed solely because no experimental test is in view: if it is interesting enough, the theory may elicit the required improvements in experimental techniques. Methodological simplicity to a moderate extent must be required, particularly from theories designed to elude or postpone *sine die* the trial of experience; if required too sternly, methodological simplicity may be obstructive to progress.

### 1.5. *Philosophical Requirements*

(*a*) *Level parsimony:* if possible, the theory should make no references to levels other than those directly involved. In any case, no jumps over levels must be made, e.g., no direct actions between mental acts and physical events, without the intermediary of organisms, should be accepted. The rule of simplicity is ambiguous in this connection as it is in others. In effect, level parsimony may be regarded as an instance of the rule; yet, what can be simpler than ontological reductionism—down, as in the case of mechanism, or up, as in the case of mentalism, both of which violate the rule of level-parsimony?

(*b*) *Metascientific soundness:* abidance by fertile metascientific principles, such as the principle of general determinacy (lawfulness plus denial of creation out of nothing). Simplicity is, in the best of cases, irrelevant to metascientific soundness—unless it is arbitrarily included among the symptoms of such soundness despite its ambiguous or negative relevance to the other desiderata of scientific theory.

(*c*) *World-view compatibility:* it is desirable, or at least desired, that the theory be consistent with the prevailing world outlook—a desideratum which, if exaggerated, leads to the banishment of originality. Simplicity is as inconsistent with world-view compatibility as it was found to be with external consistency.

### 1.6. *A Balance Sheet*

While agreement with fact as tested by experience was regarded as the sole test of a true theory,[5] simplicity alone seemed to provide the decisive criterion of choice among competing theories: empiricism was bound to lead to conventionalism and, in this way, to its own destruction. What else but simplicity could distinguish one theory from another while—in compliance with inductivism—attention was focused on empirical confirmation with neglect of all the remaining factors that, as a matter of fact, overtly or not, do intervene in the construction and evaluation of scientific theory?

The era of inductivism, phenomenalism, and conventionalism, is now ending. We have become able to recognize a score of requirements functioning, at the pragmatic level, as so many assaying criteria. And we have not included overall simplicity among them not only because nobody knows for certain what that may be (see Chapter 5), but also because a theory may be simple in some respect and false, or complex, in some regard and approximately true.

It does not seem possible to assign numerical values to the weights of the twenty requisites listed above, and it does not seem promising to attempt to quantify the contribution—positive, negative, or nil—of simplicity to those requirements. If numbers have to be mentioned, let us be content with saying that simplicity does not contribute positively to 17 out of 20 major symptoms of truth. As regards most of them, then, sim-

[5] See e.g., W. S. Jevons, *The Principles of Science* (1877), 2nd ed. (New York: Dover, 1958), p. 510, and P. Duhem, *La théorie physique,* 2nd ed. (Paris: Rivière, 1914), p. 26; see, however, p. 259, where Duhem admits that simplicity is not a sign of certainty.

plicity is similar to phlogiston: it is vague, elusive, and has a negative weight whenever it is not imponderable.

Let us now see how the above applies to a couple of recent scientific controversies.

## 2. *The Complexities of the Beta-Decay Theory*

The present theory of the beta-decay (nuclear reaction involving the emission of electrons) of neutrons, mesons, hyperons, and other so-called fundamental particles contains two hypotheses that it was found necessary to complicate in the course of time in order to square the theory with empirical data. One of the hypotheses refers to the existence of the neutrino, the other to certain symmetry properties of the basic equations.

The neutrino hypothesis may conveniently be expounded with reference to the mu-meson decay. If only charge conservation is taken into account, the hypothesis

*H1* *mu-meson* ⟶ *electron*

will be sufficient. But it is found that electrons are emitted with a continuous energy spectrum (to the extent to which observation can suggest or test continuity!); and this is inconsistent with the assumption that only two bodies are involved (if we further assume momentum conservation). *H1*, the simplest hypothesis, was therefore false; a more complex one had to be invented. The next simplest conjecture involves the introduction of an unobserved entity, the neutrino:

*H2* *mu-meson* ⟶ *electron* + *neutrino*

This hypothesis is epistemologically complex; it is also methodologically complicated because the neutrino, owing to its lack of charge and its small (or zero) mass, is remarkably elusive —to the point that many physicists have disbelieved in its existence for years, especially after many independent and elaborate attempts to detect it had failed. Still, *H2* is not complex enough: it is consistent with the continuous energy spectrum but inconsistent with the hypothesis of spin conservation, found correct in other fields. This latter hypothesis is respected by introducing a further theoretical entity, namely, the antineutrino:

*H3* *mu-meson* ⟶ *electron* + *neutrino* + *antineutrino*

This hypothesis is consistent with charge, energy, and spin conservation; but it involves an entity which a radical empiricist will regard as no less suspect than the neutrino. The decay scheme (hypothesis) has become more and more complex syntactically, epistemologically, and methodologically; at the same time a higher degree of truth has been attained.

Of course, *H3* is not the sole hypothesis consistent with the known facts; we may frame a heap of alternative conjectures just by assuming that an arbitrary number $2n$ of neutrinos and antineutrinos take part in beta-decay. But there is no point in adopting any one of these more complicated hypotheses as long as we cannot distinguish experimentally among their consequences, and as long as they do not throw new light on the explanation of phenomena. It is here that we appeal to simplicity. But we do not just choose "the simplest hypothesis compatible with the observed facts," as the inductivist methodology has it. In the first place, because none of the facts covered by the beta-decay theory is strictly observable—they are all inferred. In the second place, we select the simplest hypothesis of a set of *equally precise* assumptions, all compatible with the known *facts* and with the set of *law statements* we regard as relevant and true. And this is a far cry from unqualified simplicity; it came after a considerable sophistication and when no further complication promised to be fruitful. The rule actually used in scientific research is not just "Choose the simplest," but "Try the simplest first and, if it fails—as it normally should—gradually introduce complications compatible with the bulk of knowledge."

A second hypothesis of the theory under examination is that the laws "governing" this kind of disintegration are not invariant under the reversal of position coordinates, i.e., under the parity transformation $x \rightarrow -x$. Until the work of Lee and Yang (1956), the simplest hypothesis had been entertained regarding this transformation, namely, that all physical laws are parity-invariant (i.e., do not change under the exchange of left and right). The rejection of this statement (to be studied in Chapter 12) made it possible to identify two kinds of particles (the theta and tau mesons), which involved a taxonomical simplification; in addition, it led to predicting previously unsuspected facts, such as the assymmetry of the angular distribution of decay products (such as electrons). It will not do to count the identification of the theta and tau mesons in favor of the tenet of simplicity; this small simplification introduced in the *systematics* of fundamental particles did not involve a simplification in the basic *theory,* but was an assignment of simplicity to a corner of nature itself; it was not, in short, a case of purely semiotic simplification. Besides, it was overcompensated for by the introduction of new, less familiar terms (pseudoscalar and pseudovector contributions to the energy operator), which correspondingly complicated the theorems dependent upon them.

The theory, corrected in the ways sketched above, (*a*) had *predictive power,* (*b*) was *original* to the point of "craziness" (as both the neutrino hypothesis and the parity non-conservation hypothesis have seemed to many), and (*c*) was *deep,* to the point that it dethroned the laboriously acquired belief that no intrinsic differences between left and right could ever be detected in nature.

Not the abidance by simplicity but the bold invention of new, complicating hypotheses was decisive in the building, improvement, and acceptance of the beta-decay theory. And it is most likely that the next step will involve further complications.

## 3. *The Complexities of the Genetic Theory*

The Mendelian theory of heredity has been under attack from environmentalism, or neo-Lamarckism, since its inception. The theory of the omnipotence of the environment is attractive to many because it is so much closer to common sense, because it is causal, because (if only it were true!) it would enable us to quickly control evolution in a planned way; and last, but not least, because it is superficially compatible with an optimistic and progressive view of human life, on which nurture can overcome every shortcoming of nature. On the other hand, Mendelian genetics is formally, semantically, and epistemologically much more complex than its rival; it involves theoretical terms such as 'gene'; it calls for the use of probability theory and statistics; it does not so far afford a precise control of evolution; it suggests rather gloomy prospects and—at least in the early versions of the theory—it reinforced the anachronistic ontological tenet of the existence of an unchangeable substance (the germ-plasm). Furthermore, the genetic theory does not so far account satisfactorily for heredity in the case of higher organisms, and many geneticists are beginning to grant a parallel though weaker intervention of the cytoplasm in the transmission of characters.

Why then is Mendelian genetics accepted by most biologists? The main reasons seem to be the following: (*a*) it is *representational* or nonphenomenological, i.e., it locates precisely each hereditary factor in a bit of matter (gene, or gene complex), and it provides mechanisms (gene shuffling and mutation) that explain the final outcome, whereas environmentalism is a phenomenological theory; (*b*) it is *consistent* with the theory of evolution through natural selection (as modified to meet precisely this requirement), and with biochemistry (a plausible and precise mechanism of genetic information transmission, and of gene duplication, has recently been invented); (*c*) it has *predictive power:* statistical predictions (not individual ones) are often possible in an accurate manner with the help of its laws; (*d*) it is *refutable* and *confirmable* by experiment (e.g., mutation by direct physical action of X-rays on chromosomes), whereas the environmentalist theory is confirmable only, since it speaks about vague environmental influences; (*e*) it is *compatible* with some well-grounded and widely accepted philosophical views, such as naturalism (material basis of biological traits), and atomism (existence of discrete units of some sort on every level of organization). Last, but not least, its main enemy, Lysenkoism, has been marred by fraud, dogmatism, and unpleasant associations with curtailments of academic freedom—which, of course, has been used as an *argumentum ad hominem* against environmentalistic genetics.

Simplicity—which, incidentally, was on the side of Lysenko—played no role in the whole controversy, as compared with ideological and political considerations. Mendelian genetics is accepted, despite its shortcomings, because it is regarded as approximately true.

Further scientific theories should be subjected to the test of simplicity;[6] deep and revolutionary theories should be selected to this end, instead of insisting on the elementary case of fitting single hypotheses (e.g., polynomials) to isolated sets of empirical data—the battle horse of simplicism. It is unlikely that simplicity will be found to be a major factor of theory construction or evaluation, even though it does play a role in most theories' *advertisement*. It is unlikely, because an aim of scientific research is to uncover complexities, a task which calls for the invention of increasingly complex conceptual and empirical outfits.

## 4. *The Lightness of Simplicities*

The function of the various kinds of simplicity in scientific investigation is not as important as had been imagined by conventionalists and inductivists. There are two main reasons for the loss of weight of simplicity. The first is that *the various kinds of simplicity are not all compatible with one another and with certain desiderata of science.* Thus, a syntactical oversimplification of the basis (e.g., a drastic reduction of the number of

[6] See op. cit., fn. 3, where the theory of the planetary system, the theory of gravitation, and the theory of evolution are examined in an unsuccessful attempt to find traces of simplicism in their construction and evaluation.

primitives and axioms) may entail both difficulties of interpretation and lengthy deductions. A semantical oversimplification may involve the severance of the given theory with the remaining body of knowledge—i.e., a loss of systemicity in the sum total of science. An epistemological simplification, such as the elimination of transcendent (transempirical) terms, is not only a guarantee of the shallowness but also of infinite complexity of the postulate basis. Finally, a pragmatic oversimplification may involve a loss of insight. Consequently, it would be unwise to recommend overall simplicity even if we had an accurate notion of overall simplicity. Only trivial theories—such as the theory of the null class, or the theory of nothingness—can be simple in all respects. But are they theories?

The second reason for the devaluation of simplicism is the enormous growth of scientific theory and the accompanying realization that the task of the theoretician is not merely to describe and summarize experience in the most economical way, but to build theoretical models of bits of reality, and to test such images by means of logic, further theoretical constructions, empirical data, and metascientific rules. Such a constructive work certainly *involves* the neglect of complexities, but it does not *aim* at disregarding them. Rather, a desideratum of every new theory is to account for something that had been overlooked in previous views.

This is, essentially, why we cannot any longer believe in the scholastic maxim *Simplex sigillum veri* ("Simplicity is the seal of truth"): because we know that all our constructions are defective, hence corrigible, since, deliberately or not, they involve the neglect of an unknown number of factors. Factual theories apply exactly to schematic, impoverished models or images, and only inexactly to the real referents of these pictures. *The simpler the theoretical model, the coarser or more unrealistic it will be.* We need not wait for empirical tests in order to make sure that *all* our factual theories are, strictly speaking, false—or, put in an optimistic way, only partially true. We know this beforehand if only because *we have introduced falsities into them, in the form of simplifications,* as shown by historical experience and by an analysis of the way factual theories are built. Conceptual economy is therefore a sign and a test of transitoriness, i.e., of partial falsity—to be superseded by a lesser falsity. *Simplex sigillum falsi.*

Truth, however difficult the elucidation of this concept may be, is the central target of scientific research; hence to truth all other desiderata, including certain partial simplicities, should be subordinated. Owing to the incompatibility of the unqualified demand for economy in every respect with most symptoms of truth, simplicity should neither be regarded as mandatory nor counted as an independent criterion on a par with others, let alone above others.

Rightly understood, the rule of simplicity, far from being independent, falls under the general norm *Do not hold arbitrary (ungrounded and untestable) beliefs.* In the light of this basic rule, an arbitrary simplification is as sinful as an arbitrary complication.

The derivative character of Occam's Razor can best be seen in a couple of examples. If a biologist finds a specimen that in some respects differs from the members of a known species, he will hesitate before interpreting such variations in terms of new genera or species; he will first make sure that there are strong *grounds* for complicating the picture, not for fear of complexity but for fear of falsity. If a physicist finds more solutions than he needs for the explanation of a set of facts, he will pick up some solutions and declare the remaining solutions to be redundant. By so doing he does not apply the rule of simplicity: he eliminates certain mathematically valid solutions either because they have no physical meaning, or because they conflict with some special requirement (e.g., a boundary condition) or with some very general principle (such as the principle of antecedence, which stipulates the priority of the cause over the effect). Thus, in the Newtonian theory of gravitation the potential of a given distribution of masses is determined up to an arbitrary function; the solution is simplified by setting this function equal to zero, not out of reverence for philosophic Dadaism, but because it had previously been agreed, on physical grounds, that the potential should vanish at infinity.

These simplifications, far from obeying the rule of simplicity, fall under the rule *Do not hold arbitrary (ungrounded and untestable) beliefs.* In some cases this rule will direct the scientist to perform certain simplifications; in others it will lead him to complicate the picture by creating new, richer, conceptual tools. Only those simplifications are admitted in science which render scientific theory truer, more coherent, better testable, or more manageable; no simplification will be accepted if it severely cuts down either these characteristics or the depth, the explanatory power, or the predictive power of the theory. The difficulty of the task of truth-preserving simplifications in some definite respect can be estimated if it is recalled that economy, not poverty, is wanted. Not the simple-minded elimination of complexities is required, but a cautious reduction of redundancies, a sophisticated simplification in some regards, under the condition that it does not detract from truth and does not prevent growth.

If framed with all due precautions to prevent the mutilation of scientific theory, the rule of simplicity will boil down to the norm directing us to *minimize superfluities,* and particularly ghost-like ideas. But this rule, like every other negative injunction, is insufficient as a blueprint for the construction of theories; moreover, it does not help us to recognize which elements of a theory are redundant, i.e., which ones discharge neither a logical nor an empirical function. Productivity is not ensured by specifying what should be avoided. In short, the rule of simplicity, even if framed in an unambiguous way, is derivative and has no generative power.

## 5. *Conclusion*

*Simplicity* is ambiguous as a term and double-edged as a prescription, and it must be controlled by the symptoms of truth rather than be regarded as a factor of truth. To paraphrase Baltasar Gracián—"*Lo bueno, si breve, dos veces bueno*" ("Good and brief is twice as good")—let us say that a working theory, if simple, works twice as well—but this is trivial. If practical advice is wanted as a corollary, let this be: Occam's Razor, like all razors, should be handled with care to prevent beheading science in the attempt to shave off some of its pilosities.[7] In science, as in the barber shop, better alive and bearded than cleanly shaven but dead.

[7] A poignant illustration of the lethal potentialities of simplicism is the proposal to disregard not only what intervenes between stimulus and response, but even responses themselves. See R. C. Bolles, "Occam's Razor and the Science of Behavior," *Psychological Reports,* 3 (1957), 321.

# 8

# Partial Truth

The problem of truth has been sorely neglected by most contemporary philosophers: some have regarded it as settled, others as too difficult, and not a few have been ashamed to use the word 'truth,' fearing to be taken for old-fashioned. This neglect is unpardonable, because the concept of truth is of daily use, and science has never surrendered the search for truth, even if philosophers have occasionally proclaimed that truth had been displaced by usefulness, economy, or some other fetish. Philosophers still owe scientists a clarification of the concept of *relative and partial truth* as employed in factual science.

Scientists use two different concepts of truth: one for propositions regarded as conceptual reconstructions of certain traits of reality, another for propositions regarded as premisses or conclusions of reasoning. In the former case they view propositions as being *approximately true* or *approximately false;* in the latter case they treat those same propositions *as if* they were either altogether true or definitely false. Let us call *epistemological concept of truth* the one involved in the estimate of the material adequacy of factual propositions and—for want of a better name—*logical concept of truth* the one underlying the use of ordinary, two-valued logic and the mathematics based thereupon.

The existing theories of truth do not account for the fact that in science one and the same factual proposition is assigned at the same time *both* an epistemic degree of truth, or degree of adequacy (lying between extreme falsity and extreme truth), and a logical truth value ($F$ or $T$), according as it is viewed as a part of an account of reality, or as a piece in a logical machinery. (More often than not, the two truth values are different from one another.) This fact suggests proposing a *dualistic theory of truth,* that is, a theory introducing the notion of degree of truth while keeping ordinary (two-valued) logic. One such theory, intending to elucidate the concept of truth in factual science, will be sketched below.

## 1. *Axioms*

The theory shall enable us to compute the truth value of propositional compounds, such as $p \& q$, out of the truth values of their constituents; this is essential if the theory is to be applicable to systems of propositions and not simply to isolated sentences. Further, rules for the measurement of the truth value of the component propositions themselves shall be given.

We shall choose the $[-1,1]$ interval for the truth value $V(p/S)$ of the proposition $p$ in, or relative to, the system or theory $S$. For the sake of notational simplification we shall not mention $S$ explicitly unless more than one system comes into play. If $p$ is completely true, we shall put $V(p) = 1$; if $p$ is entirely false, we shall put $V(p) = -1$; and if $p$ is either meaningless or undecidable in $S$ (even though it may be meaningful and decidable in an alternative system), we shall put $V(p) = 0$. Values of $V(p)$ larger than 0 will be interpreted as "$p$ partially true."

Now, the building of any theory starts with a handful of "intuitive" or presystematic ideas, which play the role of desiderata to be fulfilled by the theory. Some of the "intuitions" behind our theory are the following:

(*a*) $V(-p) = -V(p)$

(*b*) If $p \leftrightarrow q$, then $V(p \,\&\, q) = V(p \vee q) = V(p)$

(*c*) $V(p \,\&\, -p) = -1$, $V(p \vee -p) = 1$

(*d*) If $V(p) = V(q) = 0$, then $V(p \,\&\, q) = V(p \vee q) = 0$

(*e*) If $V(p) \neq 0$, $V(q) = 0$, then $V(p \,\&\, q) = V(p \vee q) = V(p)$

Some of these "intuitions" may, of course, be false: i.e., they may be at variance with actual estimates of truth values. And there are further "intuitions" that the present theory does not formalize.

The above intuitive ideas are formalized in the following axiom set.

AXIOM 1. (Continuum of truth degrees.)

$$-1 \leqslant V(p/S) \leqslant 1. \tag{1}$$

AXIOM 2. (Falsity is disvaluable.)

$$V(-p/S) = -V(p/S). \tag{2}$$

AXIOM 3. (Conjunction.)

(*a*) If $V(p/S)$ and $V(q/S)$ are not both zero,

$$V(p \,\&\, q/S) = V(p/S) + V(q/S) - \frac{V(p/S)V(q/S)}{V^2(p/S) + V^2(q/S)} [V(p/S) + V(q/S) - 2\delta_{V(p),-V(q)}], \tag{3}$$

where

$$\delta_{V(p),-V(q)} = \begin{cases} 1 \text{ if } V(p) = -V(q) \\ 0 \text{ otherwise} \end{cases} \tag{4}$$

(*b*) If $V(p/S) = V(q/S) = 0$, $\quad V(p \,\&\, q/S) = 0.$ $\quad$ (5)

(If we presupposed intuitionistic logic instead of ordinary logic we would have to duplicate the number of axioms, adding to the foregoing $V(\neg\neg p) = V(p)$ and Theorems 1 and 2 below.)

The above axiom system is purely formal. The following rules of interpretation will confer a meaning upon the formulas of the calculus.

*R1.* '$V(p/S) = 1$' means "$p$ is completely true in $S$."
*R2.* '$V(p/S) \cong 1$' means "$p$ is approximately true in $S$."
*R3.* '$0 < V(p/S) < 1$' means "$p$ is partially true in $S$."
*R4.* '$V(p/S) \cong -1$' means "$p$ is almost false in $S$."
*R5.* '$V(p/S) = -1$' means "$p$ is completely false in $S$."
*R6.* '$V(p/S) = 0$' means "$p$ is meaningless, or undecidable, or undecided in $S$."

The theory can also be developed without employing the notion of worthless proposition, particularly for purposes of comparison with the probability theory of truth. In such a case the [0,1] interval may be found preferable. The corresponding expressions for the new truth values $U(p/S)$ will be obtained by means of the simple transformation formula:

$$U(p/S) = \tfrac{1}{2}[1 + V(p/S)]. \tag{6}$$

## 2. *Main Theorems*

The following consequences are immediate.

COROLLARY 1.

$$V(p \,\&\, p/S) = V(p/S). \tag{7}$$

COROLLARY 2.

$$V(p \,\&\, -p/S) = -1. \tag{8}$$

The truth values of the disjunction, the conditional, and the biconditional, are readily found from Axioms 1 to 3 with the help of the usual definitions in terms of negation and conjunction.

THEOREM 1. (Disjunction.)

(*a*) If $V(p/S)$ and $V(q/S)$ are not both zero,

$$V(p \vee q/S) = V(p/S) + V(q/S) - \frac{V(p/S)V(q/S)}{V^2(p/S) + V^2(q/S)} [V(p/S) + V(q/S) + 2\delta_{V(p),-V(q)}]. \quad (9)$$

(*b*) If $V(p/S) = V(q/S) = 0, \quad V(p \vee q/S) = 0$ (10)

COROLLARY 1. $V(p \vee p/S) = V(p).$ (11)

COROLLARY 2. $V(p \vee -p) = 1.$ (12)

THEOREM 2. (Conditional.)

(*a*) If $V(p)$ and $V(q)$ are not both zero,

$$V(p \to q/S) = -V(p/S) + V(q/S) + \frac{V(p/S)V(q/S)}{V^2(p/S) + V^2(q/S)} [-V(p/S) + V(q/S) + 2\delta_{V(p),V(q)}]. \quad (13)$$

(*b*) If $V(p/S) = V(q/S) = 0, \quad V(p \to q/S) = 0.$ (14)

(Notice the change in the Kronecker delta in formula (13); it is now equal to 1 if and only if $V(p) = V(q)$.)

COROLLARY 1. $V(p \to p/S) = 1.$ (15)

THEOREM 3. (Biconditional.)

$$V(p \leftrightarrow q/S) = \delta_{V(p),V(q)} = \begin{cases} 1 \text{ if } V(p/S) = V(q/S) \\ 0 \text{ otherwise} \end{cases} \quad (16)$$

COROLLARY 1. $V(p \leftrightarrow p/S) = 1.$ (17)

THEOREM 4. If $V(p/S) = V(q/S)$,

$$V(p \,\&\, q/S) = V(p \vee q/S) = V(p). \quad (18)$$

That is, the addition of a proposition of equal worth does not enhance the truth value of the system—although it may change some other trait, such as the unity, the scope, or the depth, of the theory.

THEOREM 5. If $V(p/S) = V(q/S)$,

$$V(p \to q/S) = V(q \to p/S) = V(p \leftrightarrow q/S) = 1. \quad (19)$$

In words: for a given value of $p$, the value of $q$ that maximizes the conditional '$p \to q$' is $V(q) = V(p)$. Even if $p$ and $q$ are each only half-true, '$p \to q$' will be altogether true in such case.

THEOREM 6. If $V(p/S) \neq V(q/S)$,

$$(a) \qquad V(p \rightarrow q/S) = -V(q \rightarrow p/S), \tag{20}$$

$$(b) \qquad V(p \leftrightarrow q/S) = 0. \tag{21}$$

The second part of the theorem follows upon application of Theorem 1 to (20) and is contained in Theorem 3, which may be read thus: equivalences are worthless unless they hold between propositions of equal value, in which case their truth value is maximal.

THEOREM 7. If $V(p/S) = -V(q/S) \neq 0$,

$$(a) \qquad V(p \,\&\, q/S) = -1 \tag{22}$$

$$(b) \qquad V(p \vee q/S) = 1 \tag{23}$$

$$(c) \quad V(p \rightarrow q/S) = -V(q \rightarrow p/S) = V(p/S) = V(-q/S). \tag{24}$$

The conjunction of propositions of truth values differing only in sign is false, and their disjunction is true, whatever their individual truth value; and the value of their conditional equals the value of the antecedent. Theorem 7($a$) encompasses the contradiction law, and Theorem 7($b$) is a generalization of the excluded middle law.

THEOREM 8. If $V(p/S) \neq -V(q/S)$,

$$V(p \,\&\, q/S) = V(p \vee q/S). \tag{25}$$

That is, the conjunction of two propositions has the same truth value as their disjunction unless their truth values are equal and opposite. This theorem is counterintuitive and therefore Axiom 3, which gives rise to it, looks suspect. In fact, since disjunction is logically weaker than conjunction we would expect that, in general, $V(p \vee q/S) > (p \,\&\, q/S)$. We shall come back to this problem in section 7.

THEOREM 9. If $V(q/S) = 0$,

$$(a) \qquad V(p \,\&\, q/S) = V(p \vee q/S) = V(p/S) \tag{26}$$

$$(b) \qquad V(p \rightarrow q/S) = -V(p/S). \tag{27}$$

THEOREM 10. If $V(p/S) = 0$,

$$(a) \qquad V(p \,\&\, q/S) = V(p \vee q/S) = V(q/S) \tag{28}$$

$$(b) \qquad V(p \rightarrow q/S) = V(q/S). \tag{29}$$

That is, the addition of an irrelevant proposition makes no difference to the system as far as its truth value is concerned; only its conceptual unity is impaired. And, if $p$ is partially true, i.e., if $V(p) > 0$, the conditional '$p \rightarrow q$' is predominantly false; in particular, if $p$ is completely true, the assertion of '$p \rightarrow q$' is entirely false whenever $q$ is meaningless. It is permissible to assert a conditional with an irrelevant or meaningless antecedent [cf. (29)], but a conditional with an irrelevant consequent will be predominantly false if the antecedent is partially true, and vice versa.

THEOREM 11.

(*a*) If $-1 < V(p/S) < 1$ and $V(q/S) = 1$,

$$V(p \,\&\, q/S) = V(p \vee q/S) = \frac{V(p/S) + 1}{V^2(p/S) + 1} > 0. \tag{30}$$

(*b*) If $-1 < V(p/S) < 1$ and $V(q/S) = -1$,

$$V(p \,\&\, q/S) = V(p \vee q/S) = \frac{V^3(p/S) - 1}{V^2(p/S) + 1} < 0. \tag{31}$$

That is, if one of the components of a binary conjunction is entirely true (false), the conjunction is predominantly true (false), regardless of the truth value of the remaining component. Application: a theory consisting of two postulates is predominantly true (false) if only one of the postulates is entirely true (false).

## 3. *Applications to Scientific Inference*

Let us begin by making sure that our theory includes deductive inference as a particular case. If $V(p \rightarrow q/S) = 1$ and $V(p/S) = 1$, i.e., if the conditions for the *modus ponens* are fulfilled, Theorem 2 yields $V(q/S) = 1$. Similarly, if the conditions for the *modus tollens* are satisfied, that is, if $V(p \rightarrow q/S) = 1$ and $V(q/S) = -1$, Theorem 2 gives $V(p/S) = -1$, as it should.

On the other hand, if $V(p \rightarrow q/S) = V(q) = 1$, Theorem 11 (*a*) yields the equation $V^2(p/S) + V(p/S) = 0$, the solutions of which are $V(p/S) = 0, -1$; nothing can then be concluded with certainty about $p$. That is, our theory does not warrant reductive inference, which again is reasonable.

Two common situations in science are the following. In the first, we tentatively assert $p \rightarrow q$, test for $q$, and ask about the degree of truth of $p$. That is, we put

$$V(p \rightarrow q/S) = 1, \quad V(q/S) = 1 - \epsilon, \tag{32}$$

$\epsilon > 0$ being, e.g., the error of observation or the level of confidence. From Theorem 2 we obtain

$$V(p/S) = V(q/S) = 1 - \epsilon \quad \text{(Confirmation)} \tag{33}$$

In words, an error in the consequent is propagated to the antecedent of a conditional; or: the antecedent cannot be asserted with more confidence than the consequent. We do not obtain conclusive verification by letting $\epsilon$ approach 0 in the above formulas.

A second frequently met situation is the one in which a prediction does not come true; in this case we have

$$V(p \rightarrow q/S) = 1, \quad V(q/S) = -1 + \epsilon, \quad \epsilon > 0 \tag{34}$$

The result is, similarly,

$$V(p/S) = V(q/S) = -1 + \epsilon \quad \text{(Disconfirmation)}, \tag{35}$$

which is a generalization of the *modus tollens.*

The intuitive notion of gradual approximation to complete truth, which is often cast in the incorrect phrase "to absolute truth through relative truths," can be elucidated in the following way with the help of our theory. Let $\{p_i\} = \{Fx_i\}$ be an ordered set of propositions $p_i \equiv Fx_i$, all with the same predicate constants lumped together in '$F$,' and containing at least one metrical predicate (numerical functor) such as, e.g., $p_i \equiv$ [length $(a) = x_i$]. Suppose further that this propositional sequence[1] is

[1] The concept of propositional sequence has been clarified by H. Reichenbach, *The Theory of Probability* (Berkeley and Los Angeles: University of California Press, 1949), p. 396.

in one-one correspondence with a numerical sequence $V(p_j)$ such that

$$V(p_j) = 1 - \epsilon_j, \quad \text{and} \quad \epsilon_1 > \epsilon_2 > \cdots > \epsilon_j > \cdots \tag{36}$$

We now renumber the $p_i$'s, calling $\{p_j\}$ the newly ordered sequence, in such a way that the successive propositions have decreasing inaccuracies. Then, we say that the propositions of the sequence $\{p_j\}$ *approach complete truth* if and only if, for any preassigned number $\delta > 0$, there exists a positive integer $N$ such that $\epsilon_N < \delta$. In such a case we write

$$\lim_{n\to\infty} V(p_n) = \lim_{n\to\infty} (1 - \epsilon_n) = 1. \tag{37}$$

This notion of propositions that "tend asymptotically to complete truth" is formally correct but materially inadequate, and this for the following reasons: (*a*) the standards of rigor and the estimates of error are not fixed once and for all but change as aims and techniques change; (*b*) the history of knowledge does show us improvements in the approximations but no uniform approaching to a limit, if only because progress is so often achieved by replacing certain sets of statements by others containing entirely new concepts; (*c*) the concept of infinity, relevant as it is to matters of fact, is entirely out of place in matters of experience.

A more realistic reconstruction of the concept of improving approximations to complete truth seems to be the following, which employs the notion of propositional sequence but postulates no limit for it. For almost all propositional sequences involving at least one metrical predicate (numerical functor),

$$(n)(\exists n')[(n' > n) \rightarrow (\epsilon_{n'} < \epsilon_n)]. \tag{38}$$

But this is just a pedantic way of saying that almost all propositions can be improved in accuracy. (The caution 'almost' is intended to cover natural limits to accuracy such as Brownian motion and finite sensorial thresholds.)

Let us finally compute the degree of association $Q(p,q)$ of two propositions as regards their degree of truth. To this end we use the positive definite function $U(p/S)$ introduced by formula (6). Yule's coefficient of association[2] then becomes

$$Q(p,q) = \frac{U(p \,\&\, q) \cdot U(-p \,\&\, -q) - U(p \,\&\, -q) \cdot U(-p \,\&\, q)}{U(p \,\&\, q) \cdot U(-p \,\&\, -q) + U(p \,\&\, -q) \cdot U(-p \,\&\, q)}. \quad (39)$$

Notice that $Q$ does not measure the logical proximity of $p$ and $q$ but rather their epistemological association. Extreme values of $Q$ are:

for $V(p) = V(q)$, $Q(p,q) = 1$ (complete association)
for $V(p) = 0$ or $V(q) = 0$ but not both zero, $Q(p,q) = 0$ (independence)

for $V(p) = -V(q)$, $Q(p,q) = -1$ (complete disassociation).

The reasonableness of these results reinforces our theory.

## 4. *Extensions of the Theory*

The above theory of partial truth can be applied to factual theories (systems of propositions referring to matters of fact) if it is agreed that the epistemic truth value of a theory is to be measured by the value of the conjunction of its postulates. This accords with actual scientific practice in so far as no theory is rejected solely because one of its assumptions is suspected or even found to be partially false. Even if no adequate substitute for the partially false assumption is found, the theory may still be of some use and will be said to contain a grain of truth. Yet, the use of a quantitative theory of the truth of theories as an instrument of decision is rather dubious, because theories are weighed as wholes and partially in connection with extra-scientific (e.g., philosophical) desiderata, as was pointed out in Chapter 7.

A more rewarding problem is that of the analysis of the empirical and theoretical components of epistemic truth. This amounts to the introduction of two different respects in which

[2] U. Yule and G. Kendall, *An Introduction to the Theory of Statistics*, 14th ed. (New York: Hafner; London: Griffin), p. 30.

a factual proposition $p$ is evaluated: as regards its empirical corroboration, and as regards its theorification, or continuity with some body of theory. (The importance of systemicity has been stressed in Chapters 6 and 7.) In short, the background $S$ against which the truth value of a proposition $p$ is evaluated can be decomposed in the form symbolically indicated by $S = ET$. We accordingly postulate the following:

AXIOM 4. (Analysis of partial truth into empirical and theoretical components.)

$$V(p/ET) = aV(p/E) + bV(p/T), \text{ with } a,b \geq 0 \text{ and } a + b = 1 \quad (40)$$

Clearly, if $p$ belongs to the theory $T$, we will put $V(p/T) = 1$; whereas, if $p$ is disproved in $T$, we shall put $V(p/T) = -1$. On the other hand, if $p$ is entirely external to $T$, we will put $V(p/T) = 0$. In short, we have

$$V(p/T) = \begin{cases} 1 \text{ if } p \in T \\ 0 \text{ if } p \notin T \\ -1 \text{ if } -p \in T. \end{cases} \quad (41)$$

Three cases are common in scientific practice. In one case, $p$ is a theorem of $T$ and has passed the test of a run of experiments to within the average discrepancy $\epsilon$; i.e., $V(p/T) = 1$ and $V(p/E) = 1 - \epsilon$, whence the total truth value is

$$V(p/ET) = a(1 - \epsilon) + b = 1 - a\epsilon > V(p/E). \quad (42)$$

(Theorification enhances the total truth value.) In the second case a known error $\delta$ has been introduced in the deduction of $p$; e.g., simplifying assumptions have been made to make an approximate computation possible. The total degree of truth is now less than in the foregoing case:

$$V(p/ET) = a(1 - \epsilon) + b(1 - \delta) = 1 - a\epsilon - b\delta. \quad (43)$$

In the third case $p$ is just a stray hypothesis of the kind studied in inductive logic, such as "All lions are fierce." In this case $p$ lacks theoretical backing, so that

$$V(p/ET) = V(p/E) = a(1 - \epsilon). \quad (44)$$

Let us now simplify the complex set of criteria actually employed in determining the adequacy of theories, by adopting the following:

CONVENTION 1. (Equal weight of empirical and theoretical tests.)

$$a = b = \tfrac{1}{2} \tag{45}$$

Axiom 4 then becomes

AXIOM 4′. $$V(p/ET) = \tfrac{1}{2}[V(p/E) + V(p/T)]. \tag{46}$$

As a consequence, formulas (42) to (44) become

$$V(p/ET) = 1 - \tfrac{1}{2}\epsilon \quad \text{(theorified hypothesis, no approximation)} \tag{42′}$$

$$V(p/ET) = 1 - \tfrac{1}{2}(\epsilon + \delta) \quad \text{(theorified hypothesis, approximations)} \tag{43′}$$

$$V(p/ET) = \tfrac{1}{2}(1 - \epsilon) \quad \text{(isolated hypothesis).} \tag{44′}$$

The maximum truth value of an isolated hypothesis is, then, $\frac{1}{2}$. This does not apply to statements about measured values, since all measurement involves various fragments of theory. The same maximum truth value would be assigned to an untested theorem of an accepted theory. This applies, e.g., to Einstein's prediction of the existence of gravitational waves. If it were found to be true, since it is not a quantitative statement (but a consequence of quantitative statements), its total truth value would become $V(p/ET) = \frac{1}{2}\cdot(1 + 1) = 1$. If, on the other hand, $p$ turned out to be empirically false, we would have $V(p/ET) = \frac{1}{2}\cdot(1 - 1) = 0$, which still is not complete falsity but rather the mark of (temporary) indecision (cf. Rule 6, section 2).

## 5. *Measurement of Empirical Truth Values*

The way empirical truth values $V(p/E)$ can be measured depends on the nature of the hypothesis $p$ and is the object of the theory of errors and the theory of statistical inference. Here we shall deal only with two elementary cases in order to show how our theory can be made to fit those theories. Let '$mV(p/E)$' designate the *empirical measure* of $V(p/E)$ on the basis of a run of observations or measurements with the help of a given set of techniques. We lay down the following stipulations.

CONVENTION 2. (Empirical truth value of instantial nonmetrical generalizations.) If, in a long sequence of $N$ tests of an instantial hypothesis of the form "All $A$'s are $B$'s," all of them equally rigorous, a total of $n$ confirming cases is found, then the measure of $V(p/E)$ is given by

$$mV(p/E) = \frac{2n}{N} - 1. \qquad (47)$$

Thus for $n = 0$, $mV(p/E) = -1$, i.e., $p$ is *empirically false;* for $n = N/2$, $mV(p/E) = 0$, so that $p$ is *empirically undecided;* and, for $n = N/$, $mV(p/E) = 1$, i.e., $p$ is approximately true as far as experience is concerned: in other words, $p$ is *empirically corroborated.* Recall that, in the absence of theoretical backing, even complete confirmation in a long run of observations, i.e., $V(p/E) = 1$, will produce at most a total truth value $V(p/ET) = \frac{1}{2}$ [see equation (44′)]. Obviously, Convention 2 can be employed only in conjunction with a rule specifying what, in the nature of the given case, can be regarded as a "long" enough sequence of observations.

CONVENTION 3. (Empirical truth value of metrical singular propositions.) If, after a long sequence of tests of a hypothesis of the form '$F(a) = b$' (e.g., "The weight of $a$ is equal to $b$," or "The probability of $a$ is equal to $b$"), the mean value $b$ is obtained with a standard error $\sigma$, then the measure of $V(p/E)$ will be given by

$$mV(p/E) = 1 - 2\frac{\sigma}{b}. \qquad (48)$$

A relative error of 50% renders a proposition of this kind worthless, and a 100% error renders it utterly false as far as experience is concerned.

The last convention is readily generalized to cover the less trivial case of the divergence between the theoretical (or predicted) value $c$, and the measured value $b$. The generalization is given by

CONVENTION 4. (Empirical truth value of metrical singular propositions obtained theoretically.) If a long sequence of tests of a hypothesis of the form '$p^T \equiv [F(a) = c]$' leads to the observational proposition $p^0 \equiv [F(a) = b \pm \sigma]$, then the measure of $V(p^T/E)$ is given by

$$mV(p^T/E) = 1 - 2\frac{|b - c|}{\text{Max }(b,c)} - 2\frac{\sigma}{b}u(c), \tag{49}$$

where

$$u(c) = \begin{cases} 1, & c \neq 0 \\ -1, & c = 0 \end{cases}. \tag{50}$$

For $b = c$, i.e., zero error, (49) reduces to (48). For $c = 0$, the second hand member of (49) becomes $-1 + 2\frac{\sigma}{b}$; this would be the case, e.g., of the empirical refutation of the prediction that no current is passing through a Wheatstone bridge. A more typical case would be $b = 100$ cm, $c = 105$ cm, $\sigma = 1$ cm; the degree of truth of the calculated value would be $mV(p^T/E) = 0.886$. Translated into the (0,1) interval by means of the transformation formula (6), we get $mU(p^T/E) = 0.943$, which corresponds to a 6% error.

Conventions 2 to 4 apply only to hypotheses of simple kinds and can certainly be improved.

## 6. *A Comparison with the Probability Theory of Truth*

Partial truth is often called probable. This denomination is correct on condition that the equation of degree of truth and probability be accepted. Unfortunately, the probability theory of truth[3] is inadequate for the following reasons.[4]

(*a*) A high truth value is often assigned to an improbable proposition. Thus, for instance, a condition for the effectiveness of induction is that the new evidence be unlikely as judged on

[3] The most elaborate system is that of Reichenbach, reference 1, Chapter 10. But the idea of equating approximate truth with probability has been in the air for centuries.

[4] Alternative reasons have been advanced by K. R. Popper, *The Logic of Scientific Discovery*, 2nd ed. (London: Hutchinson, 1959).

the basis of antecedent knowledge; i.e., if the a posteriori probability $P(h/a \,\&\, e)$ of the hypothesis $h$ given the antecedent knowledge $a$ and the evidence $e$ is to be larger than the prior probability $P(h/a)$, it is necessary that the probability of the evidence, $P(e/a)$, be less than 1, i.e., that the new evidence, even though accurately known and therefore regarded as true, be improbable. This alone should be enough to destroy the equation of probability and truth; it furthermore requires us to regard the logic of confirmation based on Bayes' formula, not as a theory of partial truth, but as a chapter of the theory of inference.[5]

(*b*) In the probability theory of truth, the truth value of a conjunction of independent propositions is, in general, smaller than the truth value of any of the members of the conjunction, since $V(p \,\&\, q) = P(p) \cdot P(q)$. In particular, a theory containing a single false postulate would be assigned zero probability and therefore zero truth value (corresponding to our $-1$). This shows that the probability theory of truth provides no adequate reconstruction of the intuitive notion of "element of truth." Our theory has the same defect in a milder form, since it assigns a negative value (but still larger than $-1$) to the conjunction of two propositions, one of which is entirely false. (See Theorem 11.)

(*c*) A condition—usually not mentioned—for the applicability of the probability theory of truth is that the truth values be assigned at random, or on the basis of the "principle of indifference"; and this is an altogether unrealistic assumption. It is on the basis of randomness that alternation is assigned a greater truth value than conjunction in that theory. In fact, it is usually said that $p \vee q$ is 3 times more probable than $p \,\&\, q$ because it may turn out true in 3 out of 4 possible cases, whereas the conjunction may be true in only 1 out of 4 possible cases. But this is true only if equiprobability is postulated or if the assignment of truth values is made by some chance mechanism,

[5] The status and value of Bayes' formula are discussed in M. Bunge, "Probabilidad e inducción," *Ciencia y técnica,* 129 (1960), 240.

as when we are gambling on the truth value of an untested proposition. And this is of no interest to science. On the other hand, randomness is not required for the application of our theory.

(*d*) In the probability theory of partial truth no room is made for irrelevant propositions, the addition of which should make no remarkable difference to a given set of statements; in other words, it is assumed that all the propositions dealt with belong to the system concerned and have some truth value; the value $\frac{1}{2}$ is made to correspond to uncertainty but not to meaninglessness or undecidability, and the conjunction of any given proposition with an uncertain proposition yields a system half as probable as the first proposition. An adequate theory of partial truth should incorporate the class of worthless propositions—which anyhow are constantly creeping in our reasonings—in order to account for the current practices of (*a*) simplifying a theory upon recognizing that it contains redundant (e.g., empirically nonsignificant) assumptions for the truth value of which no conditions are laid down in the theory, and (*b*) discarding irrelevant evidence, the inclusion of which leads, in my opinion, to the paradox of confirmation. Our theory, on the other hand, places meaningless, irrelevant, undecided, and undecidable propositions all in the same bag of epistemically valueless propositions, even though they may have some value other than truth value, and even though they may acquire a non-zero value in a different system. This is in keeping with the distinction between truth (true propositions) and knowledge of the truth (knowledge of the value of propositions), a distinction which is necessary even in formal science, e.g., in connection with undecided (but decidable) statements.[6]

## 7. *Discussion and Conclusions*

A quantitative theory has been presented which elucidates the otherwise hazy notion of partial truth and enables us to com-

[6] See M. Bunge, *Intuition and Science* (Englewood Cliffs, N. J.: Prentice-Hall, Inc., 1962), Chapter 3.

pute the degree of truth of compound propositions, hence of theories, out of the degree of truth of their constituents. The theory has the following shortcomings: (*a*) it assigns the same truth value to conjunctions and disjunctions as long as $V(p/S) \neq -V(q/S)$; (*b*) it assigns predominant falsity to a system with a single false postulate, where one would prefer having a sort of average of the truth values of the postulates; (*c*) the theory is limited to the propositional level: it does not analyze the propositions. In a more complex theory we should be able to account for the logical and semantical relations among the propositions; for instance we should be able to derive the obvious conditional '$V[(x)Fx/S] = 1 \rightarrow V[(\exists x)Fx/S] = 1$.'

At first sight our theory has two further defects. The first of them is that the function occurring in Axiom 3 has a discontinuity for $p \leftrightarrow -q$. Thus, if $V(p/S) = a$ and $V(q/S) = -a + \epsilon$,

$$V(p \,\&\, q/S) = \epsilon \left[1 + \frac{a(a-\epsilon)}{a^2 + (a-\epsilon)^2}\right] \cong \epsilon,$$

however small $\epsilon$ be compared with unity. But if $p \leftrightarrow -q$, then $\epsilon = 0$ and still $V(p \,\&\, q/S)$ does not vanish because the $\delta$ in Axiom 3 comes into play; in fact, in this case we have $V(p \,\&\, -p/S) = -1$. That is, $V(p \,\&\, q/S)$ makes a jump from almost 0 (actually, $\epsilon$) to $-1$ instead of going smoothly from $\epsilon$ to 0. This discontinuity seems absurd if we forget its origin. There is an abyss between an arbitrary pair $(p,q)$, on the one hand, and a pair of contradictories $(p,-p)$, on the other. And this logical discontinuity gives rise to the numerical discontinuity; as long as $p$ and $q$ are not mutually contradictory, $V(p \,\&\, q/S)$ is continuous, as is demanded by some "intuitions."

A second seemingly unsatisfactory trait of our theory is that it leads to a paradox. Let $T_1$ be a theory. We judge its truth value with regard to other theories—not *all* available theories but just those which are relevant to $T_1$, e.g., because they share with $T_1$ some key technical concepts. Call $T_2$ the set of theories relevant to $T_1$, and suppose we can assign a value to $V(T_1/T_2)$.

Now we ask on what basis we assign a truth value to $T_2$. Shall we say that it is on the basis of $T_1$, or on the basis of a third theory, $T_3$? We are apparently caught either in a circle or in a regress. But this is not so: we estimate the truth value of $T_2$ on the basis of another system which includes $T_1$ among other theories, since a criterion of the truth of theories is their compatibility with the rest of available knowledge. There is, then, no infinite regress. And there is no circle either: what is at stake is either a *mutual* reinforcement or a one-sided weakening of theories, and a *progressive* adjustment of theories to one another.

The following virtues of our theory may be cited: (*a*) it gives an exact (though not entirely adequate) reconstruction of the current but vague notion of partial (epistemic) truth, as a complement of the strategy of keeping fixed the extreme values 1 and $-1$ for all purposes of logical processing (e.g., the computation of predictions); (*b*) it makes room for the idea that factual truth is—like the knowledge of formal truth, though not like formal truth itself—a daughter of the times (*Veritas filia temporis*), in contrast with the constant truth value of logical and mathematical propositions; (*c*) it preserves the useful distinction between truth and knowledge of the truth, by allowing the determination of $V(p/S)$ to be an operation that does not depend on $p$ alone but also on the theoretical system $T$ to which $p$ is relevant, and on the empirical procedures $E$ with the help of which $p$ is tested; (*d*) it provides a tool for handling meaningless, irrelevant, undecided, and undecidable propositions in so far as their impact on the truth value of theories is concerned; (*e*) it does not share most of the defects of the probability theory of truth; (*f*) it can be improved as every other empirical theory can and should, whereas, on the other hand, the probability theory of truth is incorrigible, tied as it is to the rigid formalism of the theory of probability; (*g*) it is not an isolated system but is consistent with widespread epistemological views and scientific practices.

It should be realized, however, that (*a*) the assignment of precise numerical values to degrees of truth (and, for that matter, to logical probabilities as well) is in most cases pointless, owing to the large number, heterogeneity, and changeability of the symptoms and tests of truth; (*b*) a quantitative theory of truth which attempts to reconstruct some basic traits of the hazy notion of partial truth can at best be partially true itself; (*c*) the value of such a theory, if any, resides primarily in the clarification it may provide of the very concept of partial truth and cognate terms: it is a metascientific rather than a scientific tool, it may serve for the analysis rather than for the finding and accurate weighing of truth.

# III
# SCIENTIFIC LAW

# 9

# Induction in Science

Laws, the vertebrae of science, are sometimes believed to be established by induction (empiricist tradition, as represented by Bacon), and at other times to be the product of reason and free imagination (rationalist tradition, as exemplified by Einstein). The first belief is frequent among field and laboratory workers, the second among theoreticians. When the *establishment* of a law statement is mentioned, either of two entirely different inferential procedures may be meant: the *inception* or introduction of the statement, or its *test*. In either case it is accepted that inferences are involved, rather than direct and immediate apprehensions. The question is whether the inferences are inductive, deductive, or perhaps neither exclusively inductive nor exclusively deductive, but a combination of the two with the addition of analogy and of some kind of invention or creation.

In the present chapter we shall investigate the question of whether scientific inference is predominantly inductive, as claimed by inductivist metascience,[1] or predominantly deductive, as maintained by deductivism[2]—or, finally, whether it actually goes along a third way of its own. The discussion will be confined to factual statements, usually called empirical sentences, without thereby denying the great heuristic value that case examination also has in mathematical invention and problem-solving.[3]

## 1. *Induction Proper*

Before approaching the problem let us clear the ground. By *induction stricto sensu* I shall understand the type of non-demonstrative reasoning consisting in *obtaining or validating general propositions on the basis of the examination of cases.* Or, as Whewell put it long ago, "by *Induction* is to be understood that process of collecting general truths from the examination of particular facts." [4] This linguistic convention makes

[1] J. M. Keynes, *A Treatise on Probability* (London: Macmillan, 1921 and 1929); H. Reichenbach, *The Theory of Probability* (Berkeley and Los Angeles: University of California Press, 1949); R. Carnap, *Logical Foundations of Probability* (Chicago: The University of Chicago Press, 1950); H. Jeffreys, *Scientific Inference* (Cambridge: University Press, 1931 and 1957); G. H. von Wright, *The Logical Problem of Induction,* 2nd ed. (Oxford: Blackwell, 1957).

[2] P. Duhem, *La théorie physique,* 2nd ed. (Paris: Rivière, 1914); K. R. Popper, *The Logic of Scientific Discovery,* 2nd ed. (London: Hutchinson, 1959); J. O. Wisdom, *Foundations of Inference in Natural Science* (London: Methuen, 1952). Actually two of the earliest anti-Baconian works were clad in a predominantly inductivist language, as required by the "spirit of the times": I mean J. F. W. Herschel's *Preliminary Discourse on the Study of Natural Philosophy* (London: Longmans, 1830), and W. Whewell's *Novum Organum Renovatum,* 3rd ed. (London: Parker, 1858), where the first revindication of the method of hypothesis is to be found.

[3] G. Polya, *Mathematics and Plausible Reasoning* (Princeton: Princeton University Press, 1954), 2 vols. Analogy and induction in the factual sciences are still waiting for a study as masterful as Polya's.

[4] W. Whewell, *History of the Inductive Sciences,* 3rd ed. (New York: Appleton, 1858), I, p. 43.

no appeal to epistemological categories such as 'new knowledge,' which are often used in the characterization of inductive inference, although the enlargement of knowledge is the purpose of both inductive and deductive inference.

The proposed equation of induction and generalization on the basis of case examination leaves the following kinds of inference *out* of the domain of inductive inference: (1) *analogy,* which is a certain reasoning from particular to particular, or from general to general, and which probably underlies inductive inference; (2) generalization involving the introduction of *new* concepts, that is, of concepts absent in the evidential basis; (3) the so-called *induction by elimination,* which is nothing but the refutation of hypotheses found unfit because their observable consequences, derived by deduction, do not match with the empirical evidence at hand; (4) scientific *prediction,* which is clearly deductive, since it consists in the derivation of singular or existential propositions from the conjunction of law statements and specific information; (5) *interpolation* in the strict sense (not, however, curve fitting), which is deductive as well, since it amounts to specification; (6) *reduction,* or assertion of the antecedent of a conditional on the ground of the repeated verification of the consequent.

With the above definition of induction in mind, let us inquire into the role of induction in the formation and testing of the hypotheses that are dignified with the name of laws of nature or of culture.

## 2. *Induction in the Framing of Hypotheses*

The premises of induction may be singular or general. Let us distinguish the two cases by calling *first degree induction* the inference leading from the examination of observed instances to general statements of the lowest level (e.g., "All men are mortal"), and *second degree induction* the inference consisting in the widening of such empirical generalizations (leading, e.g., from such statements as "All men are mortal," "All lobsters are mortal," "All snakes are mortal," to "All metazoans are mortal"). First degree induction starts from singular propositions, whereas second degree induction is the generalization of generalizations.

Empirical generalizations of the type of "Owls eat mice" are often reached by first degree induction. Necessary, though not sufficient, conditions for performing a first degree induction are: (*a*) the facts referred to by the singular propositions that are to be generalized must have been observed, must be actual phenomena, never merely possible facts like the burning of this book or the establishment of a democratic government in Argentina; (*b*) the predicates contained in the generalization must be observable *stricto sensu,* such as predicates designating the color and size of perceptible bodies. Hence the "observables" of atomic theory, such as the variables representing the instantaneous position or angular momentum of an electron, will not do for this purpose, since they are actually theoretical predicates (constructs).

Condition (*a*) excludes from the range of induction all inventions, and countless elementary generalizations, such as those involving dispositions or potential properties. Condition (*b*) excludes from the domain of induction all the more important scientific hypotheses: those which have been called transcendent[5] or non-instantial,[6] because they contain non-observable, or theoretical predicates, such as 'attraction,' 'energy,' 'stable,' 'adaptation,' or 'mental.' Transcendent hypotheses—that is, assumptions going beyond experience—are most important in science because, far from merely enabling us to colligate or summarize empirical data, they enter into the explanation of data.

The hypothesis "Copper is a good conductor" is a second degree inductive generalization. It contains the class terms 'copper' and 'conductor' (a dispositional term). Its generalization

[5] W. Kneale, *Probability and Induction* (Oxford: University Press, 1949 and 1952).

[6] J. O. Wisdom, *op. cit.,* (fn. 2).

"All metals are good conductors" is, a fortiori, another second degree induction: it refers not only to the class of metals known at the moment it was framed, but to the conceptually open class of metals known and knowable. We do not accept the latter generalization just because of its inductive support, weighty as it is, but also—perhaps mainly—because the theoretical study of the crystal structure of metals and the electron gas inside them shows us that the predicate 'metal' or, if preferred, 'solid,' is functionally associated with the predicate 'conductor.' This association, which transcends the Humean juxtaposition of properties, is expressed in law statements belonging to the theory of solid state. We accept the generalization with some confidence because we have succeeded in understanding it, by subsuming it under a theory. Similarly, we know since Harvey that "There are no heartless vertebrates" is true, not because this statement has been found and verified inductively, but because we understand the function of the heart in the maintenance of life.

Compare the above examples with the low-level generalization "All ravens are black," the stock-in-trade example of inductivists. Ornithology has not yet accounted for the constant conjunction of the two properties occurring in this first degree induction. The day animal physiology hits upon an explanation of it, we shall presumably be told something like this: "All birds having the biological properties $P, Q, R, \ldots$ are black." And then some ornithologist may inquire whether ravens do possess the properties $P, Q, R, \ldots$, in order to ascertain whether the old generalization fits in the new systematic body of knowledge.

In summary, enumerative induction does play a role in the framing of general hypotheses, though certainly not as big a role as the one imagined by inductivism. Induction, important as it is in daily life and in the more backward stages of empirical science, has not led to finding a single important scientific law, incapable as it is of creating new and transempirical (transcendent) concepts, which are typical of theoretical science. In other words: induction may lead to framing *low-level, pre-theoretical, ad hoc* and *ex post facto* general hypotheses; the introduction of comprehensive and deep hypotheses requires a leap beyond induction.

### 3. *Induction in the Test of Hypotheses*

Scientific hypotheses are empirically tested by seeking *both* positive instances (according to the inductivist injunction) and unfavorable ones (deductivist rule). In other words, the empirical test of hypotheses includes both confirmations and unsuccessful attempts at refutation. (See Chapter 7, section 1.) But only first degree inductive generalizations *have* instances; hence they are the only ones that can be directly checked against empirical evidence. Statements expressing empirical evidence—i.e. basic statements—do not contain theoretical predicates such as 'mass,' 'recessive character,' or 'population pressure.' Hence, case examination by itself is irrelevant both to the framing and to the testing of transcendent hypotheses.

However, we do perform inductive inferences when stating plausible "conclusions" (i.e., guesses) from the examination of observed consequences of our theories. Granted, we cannot examine instances of transcendent hypotheses such as "The intensity of the electric current is proportional to the potential difference," because they are non-instantial. But hypotheses of this kind, which are the most numerous in the advanced chapters of science, do have observable consequents when conjoined with lower-level hypotheses containing both unobservable and observable predicates, such as "Electric currents deflect the magnetic needle." (The deflections can literally be observed, even though electricity and magnetism are unobservable.) And, if we wish to validate transcendent hypotheses, we must examine instances of such end-points of the piece of theory to which they belong.

To sum up, in the factual sciences the following rule of method seems to be accepted, at least tacitly: "All hypotheses, even the epistemologically most complex ones, must entail—through inferential chains as long and twisted as is necessary—instantial hypotheses, so that they can be inductively confirmed." This rule assigns induction a place in scientific method, the over-all pattern of which is admittedly hypothetico-deductive.

Inductivism rejects the deductivist thesis that what is put to the test is always some (often remote) observable consequence of theories, and that we never test isolated hypotheses but always some *pot-pourri* of fragments of various theories—eventually including those involved in the building and reading of instruments and in the performing of computations. Inductivism maintains that this description of scientific procedure might square only with very high level hypotheses, such as the postulates of quantum mechanics. However, an analysis of elementary scientific hypotheses, even of existential ones—like "There is an air layer around the Earth"—confirms the deductivist description, with the sole though important exception of the contact line between the lowest level theorems and the empirical evidence.

Consider, for instance, the process that led to the establishment of the existence of the atmosphere. An analysis of this process[7] will show that Torricelli's basic hypotheses ("We live at the bottom of a sea of elemental air," and "Air is a fluid obeying the laws of hydrostatics") were framed by analogy, not by induction, and that the remaining process of reasoning was almost entirely deductive. Induction occurred neither in the formulation nor in the elaboration of the hypotheses: it was equally absent in the design of the experiments that put them to the test. Nobody felt the need of repeating the simple experiments imagined by Torricelli and Pascal, nor of increasing their poor precision. Rather on the contrary, Torricelli's hypotheses were employed to explain further known facts and were instrumental in suggesting a number of new spectacular

[7] M. Bunge, "¿Cómo sabemos que existe la atmósfera?," *Revista de la Universidad de Buenos Aires,* IV (1959), 246.

experiments, such as Guericke's and Boyle's. Induction did appear in the process, but only in the *final* estimate of the whole set of hypotheses and experimental results—namely, when it was concluded that the former had been confirmed by a large number and, particularly, by a great variety of experiments—whereas the rival peripatetic hypothesis of the abhorrence of void had been conclusively refuted.

To sum up, enumerative induction plays a role in the test of scientific hypotheses, but only in their *empirical* checking, which is not the sole test to which they are subjected.

### 4. *Inductive Confirmation and Deductive Refutation*

Deductivists may object to the above concessions to induction, by stating that confirming instances have no value as compared with negative ones, since the rule of *modus tollens* ("If $p$, then $q$. Now, not—$q$; hence, not—$p$.") shows that a single definitely unfavorable case is conclusive, whereas no theorem of inductive logic could warrant a hypothesis through the mere accumulation of favorable instances. But this objection does not render the examination of cases worthless and does not invalidate our "concluding" something about them; hence it does not dispose of induction by enumeration.

Consider, in fact, a frequent laboratory situation, like the one described by the following sentence: "The results of $n$ measurements of the property $P$ of system $S$ by means of the experimental set-up $E$ agree, to within the experimental error $\epsilon$, with the values $x_i$ predicted by the theory $T$." Certainly, ninety favorable instances will have little value in the face of ten definitely unfavorable measured values, at least if high precision is sought. (On the other hand, a single unfavorable case against ninety-nine favorable ones would pose the question of the reliability of the anomalous measurement value itself rather than rendering the theory suspect.) But how do we know that an instance is definitely unfavorable to the central hypothesis of the theory we are examining, and not to some of the background hypotheses, among which the usual assumption may occur, that no external perturbations are acting upon our system? Moreover, do not we call "negative" or "unfavorable" precisely those instances which, if relevant at all, *fail to confirm* the theory under examination?

Confirmation and refutation are unsymmetrical to each other, and the latter is weightier than the former; moreover, a theory that can only be confirmed, because no conceivable counterexample would ruin it, is not a scientific theory. But confirmation and refutation cannot be separated, because the very concept of negative instance is meaningful only in connection with the notion of favorable case, just as 'abnormality' is meaningless apart from 'normality.' To say that hypotheses, such as natural laws (or, rather, the corresponding statements), are only refutable, but not confirmable by experiment,[8] is as misleading as to maintain that all men are abnormal.

How do we know that a skilled and sincere attempt to refute a hypothesis has failed, if not because the attempt has *confirmed* some of the lowest-level consequences of the theory to which the given hypothesis belongs? How do we know that an attempt has succeeded—thereby forcing us to abandon the hypothesis concerned provided we are able to isolate it from the piece of theory to which it belongs, and provided better ones are in sight—if not because we have obtained no positive instances of its low-level consequences, or even because the percentage of positive instances is too poor?

The falsifiabilist rule enables us to discard certain hypotheses even *before* testing them; in fact, it commands us to reject as nonscientific all those conjectures that admit of no possible refutation, as is the case, e.g., with "All dreams are wish fulfilments, even though in some cases the wishes are repressed and consequently do not show up." But refutability, a necessary con-

[8] See K. R. Popper, *op. cit.* (fn. 2), and B. Russell, *Human Knowledge* (London: Allen & Unwin, 1948).

dition for a hypothesis to be *scientific,* is not a criterion of *truth:* to establish a proposition as at least partially true we must confirm it. Confirmation is insufficient, but it is necessary.

The falsifiabilist rule *supplements* the characterization of the difficult notion of positive instance, or favorable case, but provides no substitute for it. Refutation enables us to (provisionally) eliminate the less fitted assumptions—which are those that fit the data less adequately—but it does not enable us to justify alternative hypotheses. And, if we wish to resist irrationalism, if we believe that science and scientific philosophy constitute bulwarks against obscurantism, we cannot admit that scientific hypotheses are altogether unfounded but happy guesses, as deductivism claims. Law statements do not hang in the air: they are both *grounded* on previous knowledge and successfully *tested* by fresh evidence, both empirical and theoretical.

The attitude of attempting to refute a theory by subjecting it to severe empirical tests belongs to the pragmatic and methodological level, and pertains even to the ethical code of the modern scientist. The problem of confirmation and, consequently, the problem of the degree of validation and hence of acceptability of factual theories, belong both to the methodological and the epistemological levels. There is no conflict between the procedure that aims at refuting a theory, and the assignment to it of a degree of validation, or corroboration, on the basis of an examination of positive instances: they are complementary, not incompatible operations. Yet none of them is sufficient: pure experience has never been the supreme court of science.

## 5. *Theorification*

Neither unsuccessful attempts to refute a hypothesis nor heaps of positive instances of its observable consequents are enough to establish the hypothesis for the time being. We usually do not accept a conjecture as a full member of the body of scientific knowledge unless it has passed a further test which is as exacting as the empirical one or perhaps even more so: to wit, the rational test of *theorification,* an ugly neologism that is supposed to suggest the transformation of an isolated proposition into a statement belonging to a hypothetico-deductive system. We make this requirement, among other reasons, because the hypothesis to be validated acquires in this way the support of allied hypotheses in the same or in contiguous fields.

Consider the hypothesis "All men live less than 200 years." In order to test it, a confirmationist would accumulate positive instances, whereas a refutabilist would presumably establish an enrolling office for bicentenaries—the simplest and cheapest but not the most enlightening procedure. Old age medicine does not seem to pay much attention to either procedure, but tends on the other hand to explain or deduce the given statement from higher-level propositions, such as "The arteries of all men harden in time," "All cells accumulate noxious residues," "Neurons decrease in number after a certain age," "After youth every vertebrate ceases to employ certain organs, which consequently begin to atrophy," and so on.

The day physiology, histology and cytology succeed in explaining the empirical generalization, "All men live less than 200 years," in terms of higher-level laws, we shall judge it as established in a much better way than by the addition of another billion deaths fitting the low-level law. At the same time, the hypothesis will, after theorification, offer a larger target to refutation—which is, after all, a desideratum of geriatry—since it will become connected with a host of basic laws and may consequently contact with a number of new contiguous domains of experience.

The degree of support or sustenance of scientific hypotheses —which is not a quantitative but a comparative concept (among other reasons because hypotheses have philosophical supports besides empirical ones)—increases enormously upon their insertion into nomological systems, i.e., upon their inclusion in a theory or development into a theory.

No inference can even provisionally be justified outside the context of some theory, including, of course, one or more chapters of formal logic. Factual hypotheses can be justified up to a certain point if they are grounded on deep (non-phenomenological) laws that, far from being just summaries of phenomenal regularities, enable us to explain them by some "mechanism" (often nonmechanical). Thus, the age-long recorded succession of days and nights does not warrant the inference that the sun will "rise" tomorrow—as Hume rightly saw. But a study of the dynamic stability of the solar system, and of the thermonuclear stability of the sun, as well as a knowledge of the present positions and velocities of other neighboring celestial bodies, renders our expectation highly probable. Theory affords the validation refused by plain experience: not *any* theory but a theory including deep laws transcending first degree inductive generalizations. In this way inductivism is inverted: *we may trust inductions to the extent that they are justified by noninductive theories.*

In summary, empirical confirmation is but one phase, though an indispensable, of the complex and unending process of inventing, checking, mending, and replacing scientific hypotheses.

## 6. *Inductivist Methodology and the Problems of Induction*

According to inductivism, empirical knowledge (*a*) is obtained by inductive inference alone, (*b*) is tested only by enumerative induction, (*c*) is more reliable as it is closer to experience (epistemologically simpler), (*d*) is more acceptable as it is more probable, and consequently (*e*) its logic—inductive logic—is an application or an interpretation of the calculus of probability. Deductivists[9] have shown that these claims are untenable, particularly in connection with theoretical laws, which are neither obtained nor directly tested by induction, and which

[9] Particularly K. R. Popper, *op. cit.* (fn. 2); see also "Probability Magic or Knowledge out of Ignorance," *Dialectica,* 11 (1957), 354, and "Probabilistic Independence and Corroboration by Empirical Tests," *The British Journal for the Philosophy of Science,* 10 (1960), 315.

have exactly zero probability in any universe that is infinite in some respect. They and a few others[10] have also conclusively shown that the theory of probability does not solve the riddles of induction and does not provide a warrant for inductive leaps.

All this, however, does not prove the vanity of the cluster of problems concerning induction, conceived as the set of questions connected with both the inductive inception and, particularly, the inductive confirmation of hypotheses; hence, those arguments do not establish the impossibility of *every* logic of induction, even though they considerably deflate the claims of available systems of inductive logic. It is, indeed, a fact that induction is employed in the formulation of some hypotheses both in formal and in factual science, even though it is true that such hypotheses are rarely impressive and deep. And it is a fact, too (or rather a metascientific induction!) that induction is employed in the validation of all factual theories. The mere mention of statistical inference should suffice. Now, if a subject exists, scientific philosophy suggests that the corresponding scientific (or metascientific) approach should be attempted. And why should induction be left in the hands of inductivists?

Granted, there is no inductive *method,*[11] either in the context of invention or in the context of validation; at least, there is no inductive method in the sense of a set of secure rules or recipes guaranteeing once and for ever the jump to true general conclusions out of case examination. Nor is there an intuitive method or a hypnotic method. Yet induction, intuition, and hypnosis do exist and deserve to be studied scientifically. An analysis of scientific research shows the current employment of various patterns of plausible inference,[12] such as analogy, reduction, weakened reduction, and weakened *modus tollens;*

[10] W. Kneale, *op. cit.* (fn. 5).

[11] The existence of an inductive method, claimed by empiricism from Bacon to Reichenbach, is difficulty to prove because it has never been clearly described. The safest would be to say that the method of science is not inductive.

[12] See J. M. Keynes, reference 1; G. Polya, reference 3; G. H. von Wright, reference 1; Z. Czerwinski, "Statistical Inference, Induction and Deduction," *Studia Logica,* 7 (1958), 243.

it also shows the operation of inductive policies, such as those connected with sampling, and which are after all designed to provide the best possible inductions. Why should we disregard these various kinds of nondemonstrative inference, especially knowing as we do that successful patterns tend to be accepted as rules admitted uncritically unless they are critically examined?

The rules of deductive inference, to which we all pay at least lip service, were not arbitrarily posited by some inspired genius in the late Neolithic: they were first *recognized* in sound discourse and then explicitly adopted because they lead from accepted statements to accepted statements—and statements are accepted, in turn, if they are deemed to be at least partially true. Conversely, statements that are not postulated by convention are regarded as true if they are obtained by procedures respecting accepted rules of inference. Such a *mutual and progressive adjustment* of statements and rules is apparently the sole ultimate justification of either.[13] Analogously, the belief in the possibility of a logic of plausible (nondemonstrative) reasoning rests not only on a false theory of knowledge which minimizes the role of constructs, and on a history of science biased against the theoretical, but also on the plain observation that some nondemonstrative inferences *are* crowned with success. (Usually this is the case with recorded inferences, because men, as Bacon pointed out, mark when they hit.) This is what entitles us to adopt as (fallible) rules of inference, and as inductive policies, those patterns that in good research lead from accepted propositions to accepted propositions.

Of course, the theory of plausible inference should not restrict itself to a *description* of the types of argument found in everyday life and in science: it should also refine them, devising *ideal* (least dirty) patterns of inference.[14] However, such a rational

[13] See M. Bôcher, "The Fundamental Conceptions and Methods of Mathematics," *Bulletin of the American Mathematical Society,* 11 (1905), 115, and N. Goodman, *Fact, Fiction, & Forecast* (London: Athlone Press 1954; Cambridge, Mass.: Harvard University Press, 1955).

[14] See S. F. Barker, *Induction and Hypothesis* (Ithaca, New York: Cornell University Press, 1957).

reconstruction should be preceded by a realistically oriented investigation into patterns of *actual* scientific inference, rather than by another study of the opinions of distinguished philosophers concerning the nature and role of induction.

Furthermore, ideal patterns of plausible reasoning should be regarded neither as binding rules nor as inference tickets, but rather as more or less successful, hence advisable, patterns. This, at least in the constructive stage, when the greatest freedom to imagine is needed, since creative imagination alone is able to bridge the gap separating precepts from concepts,[15] first degree inductions from transcendent hypotheses, and isolated generalizations from theoretical systems. Logic, whether formal or informal, deductive or inductive, is not supposed to concoct recipes for jumping to happy conclusions—jumps without which there is as little science as there is without careful test—but it may show which are the best patterns that can be discerned in the test of hypotheses framed in whatever way.

## 7. *Conclusion*

As must have been suspected by many, scientific research seems to follow a *via media* between the extremes of inductivism and deductivism. In this middle course induction is instrumental both heuristically and methodologically, by taking part in the framing of some hypotheses and in the empirical validation of all sorts of hypotheses. Induction is certainly powerless without the invention of audacious transcendent hypotheses which could not possibly be suggested by the mere examination of experiential data. But the deepest hypotheses are idle speculation unless their lower-level consequents receive instantial confirmation. Induction plays scarcely a role in the design of experiments, which involves theories and demands

[15] A. Einstein, "Remarks on the Theory of Knowledge of Bertrand Russell," in P. A. Schilpp (Ed.), *The Philosophy of Bertrand Russell* (New York: Tudor Publishing Co., 1944 and 1951). See also M. Bunge, *Intuition and Science* (Englewood Cliffs, N. J.: Prentice-Hall, Inc., 1962).

creative imagination; but experiment is useless unless its results are interpreted in terms of theories that are partly validated by the inductive processing of their empirically testable consequences.

To sum up, induction—which is but one of the kinds of plausible reasoning—contributes modestly to the framing of scientific hypotheses, but is indispensable for their test, or rather at the empirical stage of their test. Hence a noninductivist logic of induction should be welcome.

# 10

# Kinds and Criteria of Scientific Law

It seems to be usually believed that scientific laws can be classed only with respect to fields of research, because it is taken for granted that, from a logical point of view, law statements are all alike in being universal sentences. However, the classification of laws as regards fields of research is, save in border-zone cases, philosophically almost trivial; the requirement of strict universality takes for granted what ought to be a result of research; and the limitation of analysis to the logical structure of law statements neglects other philosophically interesting traits, such as the semantical, the epistemological, the methodological, and the ontological ones.

There are, to be sure, some exceptions: it has occasionally been acknowledged that there is a variety of kinds of law statements, and a few more or less inadequate classifications have been proposed. Even so, the kinds that have been recognized are too few, and the criteria of classification have usually not been made explicit by their authors—although every classification presupposes a selection of the property or bundle of properties in respect of which the partitioning is done. As soon as the criteria of classification, or viewpoints, are brought to light, it is realized that not only several *classes* but even various possible *classifications* of law statements are possible. In the present chapter classifications are attempted from the standpoints of four departments of philosophy, namely, semantics, formal logic, epistemology (including methodology), and ontology. A dozen major classifications will come to light—a number which should sustain no illusion of completeness.

To begin with, *lawlike statements*[1] with a factual content (to be designated '*LLS*' hereafter) will be discussed, rather than accepted law statements alone. That is, I propose to survey factual (nonformal) statements satisfying conditions necessary to qualify them as law statements—conditions such as being overtly or tacitly general in some respect and to some extent, occurring in factual science, and referring in some way or other to the regular behavior of parts of the world (including ourselves) or even to the universe as a whole. The existence of a species of *LLS* will be considered as established by merely mentioning a relevant example thereof. Yet, this survey of the kinds of *LLS* is undertaken with a more ambitious purpose, viz., to try to ascertain what, apart from a high degree of valida-

[1] The distinction between *laws* (law statements) and *lawlike* sentences occurs, e.g., in N. Goodman, *Fact, Fiction, & Forecast* (London: Athlone Press, 1954; Cambridge, Mass.: Harvard University Press, 1955), Chapter i. But whereas Goodman and other authors mean by 'lawlike sentence' any statement having all the attributes of a *universal* law save possibly truth (which laws alone are said to possess), I shall not assign a priori a definite logical form to law statements but shall rather try to find out the possible logical structures of factual propositions that smack of laws, on the rule that the elucidation of terms in current usage is not a matter of arbitrary stipulation but rather the object of an inquiry both analytical and empirical.

tion, makes a factual lawlike statement lawful—that is, what are the sufficient conditions enabling us to distinguish the subclass of law statements within the wider class of *LLS*.

## 1. *Semantical Viewpoints*

### 1.1. *Referent of 'Law Statement'* [2]

**1.1.1.** *Factual nomological statements,* or $laws_2$, are propositions the referents of which are supposed to be patterns of classes of events or processes (nomic structures, or objective laws, or $laws_1$). Nomological statements contain neither egocentric particulars like 'here' nor other specific information such as initial conditions (as in 'the velocity of this body at $t = 0$ is 1 cm/sec'); they make no reference to the operator (the knowing or acting subject, e.g., the observer) and they are assumed to be propositions about objective invariant patterns. Ex.: "Chromosomes are self-duplicating."

**1.1.2.** *Nomopragmatic statements,* or $laws_3$, are statements referring at least partly to experience and, in particular, to scientific experience; they contain pragmatic terms (such as 'measured value') and/or individual signs (e.g., egocentric particulars like 'now'), so that they can be used for controlling behavior. Many $laws_3$ are logical consequences of $laws_2$ in conjunction with pieces of empirical information; if a $law_2$ happens to be formulable as a differential equation (and we are given the corresponding rules of designation that confer a factual meaning upon the symbols occurring in the equation), then every one of the specific solutions obtained from it by integration and by specification of the integration constants (or functions) is a nomopragmatic statement. But not all nomopragmatic statements are of this sort: the quantum theory con-

[2] The genera of law statements discussed in this section were described by M. Bunge in *Metascientific Queries* (Springfield, Ill.: Charles C. Thomas, Publisher, 1959), Chapter 4. The term 'nomological statement' occurs in H. Reichenbach's *Elements of Symbolic Logic* (New York: The Macmillan Co., 1947), section 61.

tains axioms concerning the possible results of experience and, specifically, of measurement; these are nomopragmatic statements not derived from logically prior statements (such as $laws_2$), because they refer to physical systems intimately coupled with experimental devices (further physical systems). At least the following subclasses of $laws_3$ can be distinguished:

(*a*) *Predictive statements,* or statements that enable us to forecast (or to retrodict), whether accurately or not. Ex.: "If remains of pottery are found in a site, then pieces of metal can be expected in the same place." The pragmatic terms occurring in this example are, of course, 'found' and 'expected.'

(*b*) *Error statements,* or sentences about probable errors of observation or measurement. Ex.: statements about the standard error of specific law statements as checked by specified techniques. Although it is often claimed that such statements are laws of nature or at least part of them, it seems clear that they deal with our handling of law statements.

(*c*) *Methodological prescriptions:* invariant patterns of procedure that are devised for an adequate statement of scientific problems, reliable data gathering, rigorous test of hypotheses, or clean theory construction. Ex.: "Inscrutable predicates are not to be employed in science."

(*d*) *Modal nomopragmatic statements,* or statements about the physical possibility or otherwise of certain actions. These are all based on nomological statements. Ex.: "It is impossible to build perpetual movers" (follows from the first postulate of thermodynamics). Nomological statements could all be rephrased as modal sentences by sticking to them the prefix 'probably,' incorrectly meaning high degree of corroboration and, consequently, of reality. But in such a translation (which may have pragmatic advantages but obscures the logical situation) a nomological statement is transformed into a metalaw sentence: it becomes, in fact, a sentence about a law statement and, specifically, about its adequacy.

1.1.3. *Metanomological statements,* or $laws_4$, are lawlike statements about $laws_2$ or $laws_3$, expressing certain of their actual or desirable characteristics. Various subclasses can be distinguished (see Chapter 12):

(*a*) *Factual metanomological statements:* specific statements about the performance (or domain of validity) or the usefulness of $laws_2$. Ex.: "The laws of Newtonian mechanics are valid for slowly moving macroscopic bodies."

(*b*) *Normative metanomological statements* are extralogical and extraepistemological conditions imposed upon $laws_2$ and $laws_3$, and functioning as rules restricting their possible choice. Ex.: "Transition probabilities must be independent of the representation (e.g., the reference system)." Notice that statements of this kind can always be rephrased in such a way that pragmatic terms occur in them; e.g., the example above may be translated into "Transition probabilities must be independent of the observer."

(*c*) *Methodological metanomological statements* are logical or epistemological conditions imposed upon $laws_2$ and $laws_3$, and serving also as rules guiding the choice of law statements. Ex.: "Nomological statements should be consistent with the bulk of available knowledge."

### 1.2. *Referents of Specific Lawlike Statements*

**1.2.1.** *Phenomena-referent LLS:* propositions referring to phenomena or to some of their aspects, usually without either precision or depth. Ex.: "Heat flows from the hottest to the coolest bodies." This rough sort of *LLS,* typical of an early stage of science, has been commended by phenomenalism.

**1.2.2.** *Property-referent LLS:* propositions referring to constant relations among selected aspects of facts or properties of entities. The historical trend of modern science has been to replace phenomena-referent *LLS* by property-referent *LLS*—or, rather, by *LLS* containing constructs that denote properties and relations; the latter are refined explicata of the former. Ex.: "If a metal rod of length $L(0)$ is heated to the temperature $t$, its length expands to $L(t) = L(0)(1 + \alpha t)$."

**1.2.3.** *Model-referent LLS:* propositions the immediate referents of which are not actual phenomena or entities but theoretical models thereof, which are known to be more or less idealized reconstructions of facts. Strictly speaking, all quantitative theoretical law statements are model-referent in the sense that they never apply exactly to their mediate (real) referents, although they are intended to reconstruct parts thereof. Ex.: the laws of perfect gases, viscosity-free fluids, perfect conductors, etc. Science advances by increasing the number and complexity of theoretical models rather than by piling up isolated empirical data or isolated empirical generalizations.

**1.3.** *Precision*

**1.3.1.** *Coarse LLS:* more or less vague and/or ambiguous propositions such as are frequently found in the initial stages of law-finding research, e.g., in the sciences of man.

(*a*) *Predicate-imprecise LLS:* propositions containing coarse predicates, like 'hot,' which lack extensional and/or intensional precision. Ex.: "Young people's emotions are easily aroused."

(*b*) *Range-imprecise LLS:* functions to which existential quantifiers are prefixed, so that they lack a precise denotation. Ex.: "For almost all trajectories in phase space, the time averages are insensitive to the time intervals, provided the latter are large."

**1.3.2.** *Refined LLS:* propositions both predicate and range-precise. Singular or universal propositions containing least-vague predicates are precise or refined; but precision characterizes many statistical statements as well. It goes without saying that science strives for the elimination of vagueness and ambiguity, which are weeded out to the extent to which refined *LLS* are established. Ex.: "One-half of the radiocarbon atoms disintegrate in 5,100 years."

## 2. *Logical Viewpoints*

### 2.1. *Structure of Predicates*

#### 2.1.1. *Predicate Number*

*2.1.1.1. Single-predicate LLS:* propositions containing one atomic predicate.

(*a*) *Existential LLS:* limited scope propositions involving a single atomic predicate. Ex.: "There are genes."

(*b*) *Universal LLS:* unlimited scope propositions involving one atomic predicate. Apparently no *LLS* of this kind are found in science. *LLS* like "Everything flows" can be found, on the other hand, in ontology.

*2.1.1.2. Multiple-predicate LLS:* propositions in which various predicates occur.

(*a*) *Existential LLS:* limited scope propositions involving two or more predicates. Ex.: "There are substances which are not attacked by hydrochloric acid."

(*b*) *Universal LLS:* unlimited scope propositions involving two or more predicates. Ex.: "All bodies attract each other with an inverse square force."

#### 2.1.2. *Number of Argument Places (Degree)*

*2.1.2.1. One place predicate LLS:* propositions involving monadic predicates only. Ex.: "Division of labor increases with population."

*2.1.2.2. Many-placed predicate LLS:* propositions involving relations. Ex.: *LLS* involving interpreted mathematical functions. Most laws, when written in full, contain relations.

#### 2.1.3. *Predicate Order*

*2.1.3.1. First order predicate LLS:* propositions containing nothing but predicates denoting properties of individuals. Most law statements are of this kind.

*2.1.3.2. Higher order predicate LLS:* expressions containing second or higher order functions (designating classes of properties or properties of properties). Ex.: "Thermodynamic properties almost do not depend on the initial microstates of the individual components of the systems concerned."

2.1.4. *Metrical Character*

*2.1.4.1. Nonmetrical predicate LLS:* propositions containing only class or order predicates, such as 'gas' or 'later.' Ex.: "The energy levels of stable systems are discrete." Most *LLS* in the sciences of man, as well as the model microlanguages constructed by logicians, allow for such predicates only.

*2.1.4.2. Metrical predicate LLS:* propositions involving numerical variables, such as 'length' or 'IQ.'

2.1.5. *Distributivity*

*2.1.5.1. Distributive predicate LLS:* propositions containing distributive predicates only, such as 'extended' or 'material,' that are true of all the constituents of the referents. Ex.: the basic equations of the quantum theory.

*2.1.5.2. Global predicate LLS:* propositions in which predicates such as 'liquid' or 'living' occur, which are not true of all the constituents of the referent. Ex.: statements in which the terms 'composition,' 'average,' 'density' and the like occur.

2.2. *Extension or Range*

2.2.1. *Particular LLS:* propositions containing individual signs (proper names, definite descriptions, egocentric particulars, and the like) or beginning with existential quantifiers ('there are,' 'many,' 'most,' etc.).

*2.2.1.1. Singular LLS,* or pseudosingular sentences: propositions containing singular terms but also, in a tacit way, bound variables of unlimited scope. The referents of such sentences are individual objects (e.g., the sun), but some of the properties attributed to them by the *LLS* are supposed to be true either for all places within a given volume or for all times within an interval. Ex.: "The (natural) moon rotates around the earth." The hidden time variable is here supposed to take on an infinity of values within an interval. Such pseudo-singular statements with hidden universal scope in some respect are often found in the initial stages of theory construction and in the lowest levels of full-fledged theories; they abound, of course, in common-sense discourse. On the other hand, a sentence like "Life emerged about two billion years ago" is genuinely singular if, as usually construed, it is taken to refer to a single bit of living matter. However, one should not overlook the fact that it contains universal words like 'life,' so that it is intensionally lawlike.

*2.2.1.2. Existential LLS,* or expressions in which existential quantifiers occur ostensibly at the beginning.

(*a*) *Indefinite existential LLS:* statements of unqualified existence. Ex.: "There are living bodies in which silicium takes the place held by carbon in ordinary living matter." Here again time quantification is silently assumed: while referentially existential (since the ostensive quantifier binds the object variable), these *LLS* are universal in respect to space and/or time. Few philosophers have regarded such statements as laws;[3] at any rate they presuppose laws and, in turn, may serve as premises in deductive arguments.

(*b*) *Localizing existential LLS:* statements of local existence, but tacitly quantified with respect to time. Ex.: "There is practically no atmosphere beyond 1,000 Km altitude."

*2.2.1.3. Statistical LLS:* propositions denoting regularities in large or in the long run. They contain logical

[3] N. Campbell, *What Is Science?* (London: Methuen, 1921; New York: Dover Publications Inc., 1952), p. 41, regarded "There are magnets" as a law asserting that certain properties are invariably associated. H. Reichenbach, in his posthumous work *Nomological Statements and Admissible Operations* (Amsterdam: North-Holland, 1954), Chapter iii, acknowledged existential laws but maintained that they are all derived. However, the property of being derived is contextual, not absolute; besides, a proposition such as "There are neutrons," far from being a theorem of nuclear physics, was a hypothesis launched by experimentalists and has become a presupposition of nuclear theory.

constructs belonging to mathematical statistics and characterizing central or over-all trends ('average,' 'dispersion,' 'correlation,' and the like). Ex.: "The most frequent value for family size in the Western hemisphere is two children."

*2.2.1.4. Quasi-general LLS:* propositions allowing for exceptions, whether specifying them or not. Ex.: many theorems in statistical mechanics, in which the phrases 'in most cases,' 'almost all points,' 'to any desired degree of accuracy,' and the like occur (e.g., Poincaré's theorem of almost-recurrence). The laws of society and history (e.g., "In most societies matriarchate precedes patriarchate") are of this kind. If sociologists and historians realized that statistical physics is full with such laws, they would not be ashamed of calling laws their own generalizations. Sentences making allowance for definite exceptions—e.g., "$(x)(x \neq a \rightarrow Fx)$"—have occasionally been studied by logicians.[4] But quasi-general *LLS* of interest in science rarely, if ever, exclude specific individuals; rather, they exclude unspecified individuals or specified classes, and the rate of exception is not always stated.

2.2.2. *Universal LLS:* expressions containing ostensible universal quantifiers in respect to their referents, but of various extensions in respect to spacetime.

*2.2.2.1. Pseudouniversal LLS,* or point-like *LLS:* propositions of universal form involving singular terms. Ex.: "The compass needle never attains a stable position in the neighborhood of the magnetic poles."

*2.2.2.2. Regional and/or epochal LLS:* propositions applying to a finite number of instances or to a limited continuous range. Ex.: particular biological, sociological, and historical *LLS* (referring to definite species, groups, regions, periods, etc.). It is common knowledge that regional and/or epochal *LLS* (like "Among all aboriginal peoples, important actions give rise to ceremonial behavior") are typical of socio-

[4] See R. Carnap, *Logical Foundations of Probability* (Chicago: University of Chicago Press, 1950), section 37.

historical science. But all laws of nature might be local and/or temporary.

2.2.2.3. *Strictly universal LLS:* statements of infinite scope. Ex.: the so-called fundamental laws of physics. Logicians usually assume that only strictly universal *LLS* are called law statements. But laws of thermonuclear reactions do not apply in cold clouds, and the laws of biology did not emerge before the origin of life. Universality *de jure* but not *de facto* seems as worthless as bishoprics *in partibus infidelius.*

**2.3.** *Systemicity*

**2.3.1.** *Isolated LLS:* propositions not embodied in a theory and having consequently at most the support of their instances. Ex.: empirical generalizations such as "Water quenches thirst" before being explained by physiology.

**2.3.2.** *Systematic LLS:* propositions belonging to theories.

(*a*) *Axiomatic LLS:* propositions that occur as principles in a given context (theory). Ex.: Schroedinger's equation in conventional quantum mechanics. Since the distinction between basic and derived statements is contextual (i.e., relative to a theoretical context *T*), we ought to relativize it explicitly by saying, e.g., "*L* is axiomatic in *T*" (see Chapter 2).

(*b*) *Theorematic LLS* or derivative *LLS:* propositions derived from logically prior propositions in a given system. Ex.: the law of the simple pendulum in the context of Newtonian mechanics.

**2.4.** *Inferential Power*

**2.4.1.** *Specification or Instantiation*

(*a*) *Specifiable LLS:* propositions allowing the direct inference of singular (particularly, observational) statements by specification, i.e., upon replacement of variables by constants. Ex.: theoretical derivative *LLS,* such as the solutions of the fundamental equations of physics.

(*b*) *Conditionally specifiable LLS:* propositions that are not specifiable in the same terms but require syntactical and/or semantical transformations before allowing specification. Ex.: the equations and inequations of factual science must be solved (syntactical transformation) and interpreted (semantical operations) before anything definite can be concluded about individual cases.

(*c*) *Unspecifiable LLS:* propositions that do not allow the drawing of singular statements by specification, even after syntactical or semantical transformations. Ex.: statistical *LLS* containing essentially nondistributive (global) predicates such as 'average' or 'standard deviation.'

2.4.2. *Counterfactual Force*

(*a*) *Counterfactually powerless LLS:* propositions that do not sustain counterfactual inferences. From "All the books in the Dean's library are serious" it does not follow that, if the *Decameron* were in the Dean's library, it would be a serious book. Ex.: statistical laws such as "Nearly half of the population consists of males." Logicians have claimed that counterfactually powerless *LLS* should not be counted as laws.[5]

(*b*) *Counterfactually powerful LLS:* propositions sustaining counterfactual inference. Ex.: "Venus rotates around the sun," from which we can infer "If that comet were Venus it would rotate around the sun."

## 3. *Epistemological Viewpoints*

### 3.1. *Inception*

3.1.1. *Analogically found LLS:* propositions inferred by means of arguments from analogy. Two kinds of analogical inference can be distinguished: from particular to particular (first degree analogy), and from general to general (second degree

[5] N. Goodman, *op. cit.,* fn. 1, Chapters i and ii. R. M. Chisholm, "Law Statements and Counterfactual Inference," *Analysis,* 15 (1955), 97.

analogy). Obviously, only the second kind of analogy can produce statements general to some extent and therefore candidates for lawfulness. Ex.: the central hypothesis of the nuclear shell model was conceived in analogy with the atom model.

3.1.2. *Inductively found LLS:* generalizations on the basis of case examination. Inductive generalizations are found mainly in the presystematic stage of a discipline (see Chapter 9).

3.1.3. *Deductively found LLS:* propositions deduced from other statements, whether validly or not. The following subclasses may be distinguished:

(*a*) *Theorems:* statements deduced from the axioms and definitions of a theory. Ex.: laws concerning averages and dispersions, when derived from "elementary" laws regarding individuals.

(*b*) *Derivations from wider scope theories.* Ex.: the formula for the specific heat of solids as deduced from the general principles of quantum mechanics in conjunction with a model for solids.

(*c*) Partial derivations from theories of a different field. Ex.: the cosmological fantasies on the origin and annihilation of the universe contain premises belonging to myth and religion.

3.1.4. *Invented LLS:* constructions, guesses framed in order to explain empirical data, or speculations about possible facts or experiences. Ex.: Maxwell's equations.

### 3.2. *Ostensiveness*

3.2.1. *Empirical LLS:* propositions in which only observation predicates occur. (That is, strictly observable properties are designated by the corresponding predicates; in this sense, densities and field strengths are not observation predicates.) Empirical *LLS* are either generalizations of observed relations, or are derivable from conjunctions of lowest-level theorems with specific information.

(*a*) *Manifest-predicate LLS:* propositions containing only manifest (non-dispositional) observable terms, like 'position,' 'displacement,' and 'white,' with reference to macroscopic accessible bodies.

(*b*) *Observable dispositional-predicate LLS:* propositions containing terms designating observable dispositions, to the extent to which any disposition can be regarded as observable and not as inferred. Ex.: "Workers spend more on food than do clerks with the same income." The dispositionals are clearly 'worker' and 'clerk'; what is not clear is that they are strictly observable.

3.2.2. *Transcendent LLS:* propositions containing transcendent (transempirical) predicates, or intervening variables. These may be theoretical predicates (e.g., 'mass'), inferred entities (e.g., 'planet orbit'), or logical constructs (e.g., 'density'), whether open to (indirect) scrutiny or not. In other words, transcendent *LLS* contain terms that could not occur in the evidence (observation statements) of any factual hypotheses.

(*a*) *Inscrutable-predicate LLS:* propositions denoting entities the existence of which cannot be ascertained by any empirical means—such as *élan vital* or *id*—so that they should be shaven with Occam's razor. Ex.: expressions in which the terms 'absolute velocity of bodies' or 'libido energy' occur. Although inscrutable predicates have often been introduced in the preliminary stages of science (remember 'phlogiston,' 'caloric,' and 'ether') and will probably continue to be, they are finally expelled from scientific discourse or are elucidated in terms of scrutable predicates (e.g., via law statements), because they lead to the formation of untestable assumptions. Inscrutable-predicate *LLS* are, therefore, either prescientific or unscientific.

(*b*) *Scrutable-predicate LLS:* propositions containing only scrutable (but not necessarily observable) predicates, and independently scrutable at that. Some such scrutable transcendent predicates are found in ordinary language, in which quite a few behavioral law statements are couched (e.g., "Language adapts itself to life and culture patterns and tends in turn to conserve them"). But in the advanced stages theoretical transcendent predicates, such as 'electric current,' 'energy,' and 'sensory threshold,' are introduced.

### 3.3. *Testability*

**3.3.1.** *Exclusively confirmable LLS:* propositions that are confirmable but irrefutable, i.e., statements for which favorable evidence can be gathered, but which cannot be refuted. Ex.: indefinite existential *LLS* such as "There are signals faster than light." It has been contended [6] that, in contrast to localizing existential hypotheses, those existential hypotheses which do not specify place and time are nonempirical or metaphysical because they are irrefutable. This must be conceded if it is previously agreed that the sole test of scientific hypotheses is deductive, i.e., along the line of attempting to refute observational consequents after the pattern of the *modus tollens*. That indefinite existential hypotheses are irrefutable (given time) is obvious; that they are nonempirical or extrascientific must be denied: suffice to recall the importance for research of predictions like "There are transuranium elements," the working hypothesis with which Fermi began his most important work. "There are atoms," "There are genes," "There are neutrinos," and other similar assumptions have not been wild metaphysical conjectures but testable physical hypotheses—only, they were exclusively confirmable. Moreover, all singular propositions (e.g., observation statements) warrant the direct inference of existential statements, which are in turn negations of universal propositions. The fact that there *are* irrefutable (but confirmable) scientific hypotheses shows that the criterion of refutability, indispensable as it is in connection with *universal* statements, must be relaxed for existential hypotheses and as a consequence cannot be required from the whole of science.

[6] K. R. Popper, *The Logic of Scientific Discovery,* 2nd ed. (London: Hutchinson, 1959), section 15.

3.3.2. *Confirmable and refutable LLS:* propositions that can be established both by cumulative favorable evidence (instance confirmation and reductive inference), and by failures of attempts to refute them or some of their consequences. These are the most common in science.

(*a*) *Directly testable LLS:* propositions containing perceptual terms only, and consequently testable by inspection, introspection, or manipulation, without recourse to other propositions. Those pseudosingular and existential *LLS* that contain observation predicates only are directly testable. Ex.: "The Southern Cross is visible from Argentina."

(*b*) *Inductively testable LLS:* propositions that must be supported by other propositions (singular observation statements) that either match with them or fail to refute them. This is the case with all generalizations, whether empirical or theoretical. Some can be tested by checking sets of more or less distant consequents against empirical evidence (such was the case of Maxwell's hypothesis of displacement currents in vacuum and dielectrics); others can be tested by comparison with accepted theoretical statements (e.g., variational principles in field theory are checked by means of given field equations).

## 4. *Ontological Viewpoints*

### 4.1. *Levels*

4.1.1. *One-level LLS:* propositions denoting patterns of occurrences on a single level or sublevel of reality. Ex.: historical law statements in which neither biological nor psychological nor economical categories occur.

4.1.2. *Multilevel LLS:* propositions denoting patterns of occurrences on two or more levels or sublevels of reality.

(*a*) *Lower-level referent LLS:* propositions connecting properties of a given level to properties belonging to lower levels or sublevels. Ex.: the laws of biophysics and psychochemistry.

(*b*) *Higher-level referent LLS:* propositions connecting properties of a given level to properties belonging to higher levels or sublevels. Ex.: "The demand of commodities may fluctuate owing to changes in taste."

(*c*) *Adjoining-level referent LLS:* propositions concerning properties of adjoining levels. Ex.: the laws of social psychology.

4.2. *Determination Categories*

4.2.1. *LLS Free from Determination Categories*

(*a*) *LLS of irrelevance:* propositions asserting that a given factor (variable) makes no difference to other factors. Ex.: "The acceleration of gravity does not depend on the nature or on the mass of the test body." All universal *LLS* can be construed as statements of irrelevance with regard to specific spacetime regions: a variable bound by an all-operator is in a sense an irrelevant variable, and a law of conservation may be read as a statement of irrelevance relatively to the "flow" of time. But, in order to be placed in this class of *LLS*, a proposition should include no determination category. The relation between scientific *LLS* of irrelevance and nonscientific lawlike and even true sentences, like "The average nose length in a nation does not depend on its index of illiteracy," will be discussed in the last section.

(*b*) *LLS of accidental relationship:* propositions about coincidences believed to occur by chance or because of a common source. Ex.: numerical relations among physical constants can be found in any number and to any desired degree of accuracy by patiently juggling with numbers and units (Eddington's game).

(*c*) *Taxonomical LLS:* propositions about class inclusion or ordering among natural kinds. Ex.: the periodic chart of the elements. Notice that, since all *LLS* state relations among properties, and since properties determine classes, all law statements can be construed, though with no obvious advantage, as taxonomical; but what we are calling taxonomical *LLS* are nothing but statements of class relations.

(*d*) *LLS of correlation:* statements of statistical tendencies toward association of attributes. Ex.: "Cancer is more frequent among older people than among young people." Some *LLS* serve as cues for establishing law statements containing determination categories, such as causal laws (see Chapter 11).

(*e*) *LLS of association* of attributes, or coexistence of characters. Ex.: equations of state.

(*f*) *Morphological LLS,* or propositions regarding shape and symmetry. Ex.: "The higher a living form, the less symmetrical is the arrangement of its internal organs." Contemporary biological morphology does not restrict itself to describing forms and their development: many of its law statements include determination categories; a typical instance is the schema "Each *X*-developmental process in species *Y* arises from the set of factors *Z*." Hence, the laws of biological morphology are not all of them purely morphological *LLS*.

(*g*) *Laws of composition* or distribution: propositions regarding the constitution of collections or wholes. Ex.: frequency diagrams.

(*h*) *Structural LLS:* propositions denoting unchanging spatial configurations. Ex.: chemical structural formulas, such as "*H-O-H*."

(*i*) *Conservation LLS:* assertions of time invariance of attributes. Ex.: "The number of chromosomes in each biological species is constant."

(*j*) *Extremum LLS:* propositions asserting that certain quantitative variables (usually unobservable) have a minimum or a maximum value. Ex.: the principle of stationary optical path.

(*k*) *Transformation formulas:* sentences relating variables in different reference systems or in different representations. Ex.: Lorentz' transformations.

(*l*) *Kinematical LLS:* propositions denoting particular patterns of sequence. Ex.: learning and forgetting curves.

(*m*) *Global trend kinematical LLS:* propositions regarding overall trends of evolution. Ex.: "All systems tend to approach a state of equilibrium."

4.2.2. *LLS involving determination categories*

(*a*) *Self-determination LLS:* propositions accounting for change in terms of inner (noncausal) determiners. Ex.: principles of inertia in various chapters of science.

(*b*) *Causal LLS:* statements of the form 'If *C* happens, then (and only then) *E* is always produced by it,' where '*C*' designates a class of factors or changes external to the system under consideration (see Chapter 11). Ex.: "Electric fields deflect the trajectories of charged particles." Most of the so-called causal laws have at most a causal range or a causal approximation; in other ranges alternative determination categories are dominant. Something similar may hold for laws of other types.

(*c*) *Interaction LLS:* propositions denoting the mutual action of different entities or aspects of entities. Ex.: Newton's law of universal gravitation.

(*d*) *Dynamical LLS:* propositions regarding forces exerted upon or by bodies. Usually self-movement, causation, and interaction categories occur in these *LLS*. Ex.: Newton's second law of motion.

(*e*) *Trigger-action LLS:* propositions denoting events or processes started by some event or agent which is in some respect out of proportion to the size of the effect. Ex.: generalizations on auxin-induced reactions in plants.

(*f*) *Blocking-action LLS:* propositions denoting the blocking or the interruption of a process (e.g., a cycle) by some agent. Ex.: "Carbon monoxide blocks the oxygen transport by hemoglobin in blood."

(*g*) *Global dynamical LLS:* propositions referring to factors acting in the shaping of overall trends. Ex.: "Systems initially in equilibrium tend to react to external disturbances in a way that decreases the latter's effect."

(*h*) *Dynamical statistical LLS:* propositions denoting the results of the interplay of numerous nearly independent co-existent entities, or strings of weakly chained events. Ex.: stochastic relations, such as those occurring in the theory of Brownian motion.

(*i*) *Dialectical LLS:* propositions concerning the emergence of qualitative novelty as a result of external or internal mutual actions. Ex.: "New knowledge arises from the clash of hypotheses with one another and with empirical evidence."

(*j*) *Teleological LLS:* propositions denoting processes that are assumed to be subordinated—in the main and in the long run—to one or more ends. Ex.: "Most organs develop and maintain themselves in order to fulfil useful functions, and most functions serve useful purposes."

## 5. *Criteria of Laws*

More than seven dozen not mutually exclusive kinds of *LLS* have been recognized and baptized. We may now approach two important questions: (1) Which of them are as a matter of fact called law statements (or simply laws)? (2) Which deserve the title of law statements even though for some reason—for instance, historical origin, or philosophic blindness—they may, as a matter of fact, be called by other names, e.g., rules? The first question might best be answered by an empirical investigation about the lawlike statements that the majority of practicing scientists of our time would be prepared to honor with the title of law. The second question is not a *de facto* but a *de jure* one; if admitted as a sensible question at all, it will call for a decision—based, if possible, on the answer to the previous question—about the conditions that lawlike statements ought to fulfil in order to be promoted to the rank of law statement. Let us see what the preceding sections have to say on both questions.

The semantical approach (section 1) seems to raise but one serious problem, namely, if methodological prescriptions (1.1.2.*c*), modal nomopragmatic statements (1.1.2.*d*), normative metanomological statements (1.1.3.*b*), and methodological metanomological statements (1.1.3.*c*) are to count as laws, then obviously laws must not be required to have truth or even a high degree of confirmation, but only fertility and consistency with corroborated statements. Conversely, if truth (or, rather, a high degree of truth) is required from all law statements, then the above mentioned kinds of *LLS* cannot be regarded as laws. The latter course seems advisable if we wish to conform to accepted usage. But, then, let us be consistent and stop calling modal statements like "Physical laws must be independent of the observer's state of motion," physical laws; they are metalaws in the nature of norms or prescriptions. The remaining kinds of *LLS* mentioned in section 1 seem to be serious candidates for law statements; but, of course, not all of them denote laws of nature or culture.

The logical approach (section 2) raises three major problems. The first is the inclusion of statements of limited scope (singular, existential, and numerically universal *LLS*). Many would prefer to call these statements simply scientific hypotheses, which they certainly are, even after validation. Yet, it may be argued, in the first place, that the above mentioned *LLS* are tacitly universal in some respect, even though at first blush they look like entirely particular sentences; in fact, even though referentially limited (e.g., "Hume was a sybarite"), they are supposed to be temporally or spatially universal in some domain—this being why they were nominated as candidates. In the second place, the difficulty in finding strictly universal laws, nonvacuous in every volume of spacetime, sounds like an invitation not to be too exacting in requiring strict universality (both referential and spatiotemporal)—unless we are ready to find out some fine day that not a single nomological statement remains that strictly qualifies for lawfulness.[7] In the third place, a referentially universal *LLS*, highly esteemed by many philosophers, like "All ravens are black," is surely as little entitled to bear the title of

[7] See H. Mehlberg, *The Reach of Science* (Toronto: University of Toronto Press, 1958), p. 162.

law as is a deep and fruitful—but, alas, merely existential—hypothesis such as "There are forms intermediate between the living and the nonliving." The ostensible logical form may not be as important as the depth, fruitfulness, and systemic status of a scientific hypothesis.

The second important point concerns systemicity and, specifically, the status of isolated lawlike statements like the one about ravens. We often call them, in a contemptuous mood, "mere empirical generalizations," thereby accepting the fact that systemicity is a decisive test of hypotheses; or, if preferred, we admit that belonging to some body of theory is a necessary condition for a hypothesis to be ranked as a scientific law. Since system is a defining property of science, it seems reasonable to require systemicity of law statements or, conversely, to refuse to confer the title of law upon isolated *LLS,* whatever their degree of universality.

The third important question regards the requirement, sometimes mentioned, that law statements, in contradistinction to statements of accidental generality, ought to warrant counterfactual inference. Now, statistical and taxonomic *LLS,* which may otherwise have good titles to lawfulness, do not all comply with the requisite of counterfactual force. The possibility of counterfactual inference may be helpful in another connection, namely, as a criterion for telling real generality ("All men are mortal") from accidental generality ("All readers of this book are out of luck"); but it is not applicable to particular *LLS,* which it would be unprofitable to regard as denoting mere coincidences or contingent states of affairs. Hence, we shall drop the condition of counterfactual force as being neither necessary nor sufficient.

The epistemological classifications (section 3) seem to raise no perplexities: since the bankruptcy of inductivism has become evident, we do not ask about the previous adventures of hypotheses before espousing them; they all become respectable upon validation. And the requirement of testability imposes the rejection of statements containing inscrutable predicates, which seem to be the sole undesirable ones listed in this section—unless phenomenalism were adhered to, in which case all transcendent-predicate *LLS,* i.e., the deepest part of science and the most effective, would be thrown overboard.

The ontological classifications (section 4) should prove perplexing and even irritating to conjunctivists and necessitarians alike, because they suggest that law statements do not necessarily denote either constant conjunctions or causal bonds. One problem raised by this approach is how to tell a law of irrelevance from an *LLS* of irrelevance (cf. 4.2.1.*a*). Nobody would regard the biuniversal truism "Boiling temperatures and social structure are mutually independent" as a worthy law of nature, whereas "The initial positions and velocities of the molecules in a gas are irrelevant to its final equilibrium state" is rated as a law. Is there an intrinsic difference at stake, or is it a question of circumstances and, perhaps, of world-view? It would seem that statements of irrelevance are called laws when they happen to occur either in the criticism of prevailing theories (as was the case with Galileo's statement of the irrelevance of shape and composition to the acceleration of falling bodies), or as theorems in accepted theories. In the latter case one often starts from the assumption that a relation of relevance could conceivably hold; special techniques are then applied to test the possible relation (e.g., differentiation and the chi-square test) and, if the hypothesis is refuted, the resulting statement of irrelevance is often promoted to the rank of law. At other times one directly binds the undesirable variables by means of procedures such as summation, integration, and averaging, and finally tests the result thus obtained. There do not seem to exist fixed rules for deciding to call law a statement of irrelevance, apart from pragmatic considerations such as surprise and fertility.

Another problem raised by the ontological classification is how neat the distinction between necessary and accidental relationship (cf. 4.2.1.*b*) can be. Since we know from experience that some *LLS* of accidental relationship eventually turn out to be full-fledged law statements (and vice versa), we ought to be cautious in dismissing them all. Granted, we shall decide not to accept them as denoting laws, because they are not backed by further laws (they lack systemicity); but instead of sending them to the hell of error we may place them in the limbo of doubtful propositions (working hypotheses) awaiting the day of judgment —which anyway never comes for factual hypotheses.

The last important problem occurring in section 5 is also the most difficult; it concerns the status of conservation *LLS* (cf. 5.2.1.*i*), which conventionalism has regarded as disguised definitions or as tautologies. Although this is not the place to deal with this problem in detail, the following must be said. In the first place, the general principles (actually, theorems) of energy (or rather energy-momentum) and angular-momentum conservation, unlike other *LLS* of conservation, look like irrefutable conventions or as platitudes because, as soon as an exception to them is found, we add a new term ensuring conservation of the sum total. But this new term, denoting a new kind of energy or of angular momentum, is independently checked by experiment and happens to be a key concept in some theory—a concept linked to basic variables via further law statements, and not just a stray symbol introduced *ad hoc*. Hence its introduction is not just a convenient fiction enabling us to reassure ourselves that something is conserved in the flux of phenomena: the concept does denote an important objective property. Secondly, in every physical theory we find a fixed number of conservation equations (yielding one constant of the motion each); thus, in analytical mechanics of the mass point there are seven such equations, and their number cannot be increased arbitrarily—whereas, on the other hand, conventions can be multiplied *ad libitum*. Thirdly, almost every law statement can be used as a definition of some concept in terms of other concepts; the question is to ascertain whether, *besides* being usable as a definition, the statement happens to be true. And this seems to be the case with conservation laws, which are empirically testable.

We may now try to find out what criteria or requisites of lawfulness should count without danger of mutilating the corpus of science or of inhibiting research in the younger sciences. An obvious requisite is *genuine generality in some respect* (referentially and/or spatiotemporally, in an ostensible or in a tacit way);[8] this characteristic is not common to all scientific hypotheses (especially if we class among them observation reports, since they are corrigible), but it is shared by all lawlike statements. A second equally obvious requirement—obvious, that is, in view of current usage—is *empirical corroboration* in some domain and with a precision consistent with available techniques. This condition presupposes aposterioriness, or empirical import, or factual reference; it is enough to exclude from the class of scientific laws propositions like '$(x)(x \neq x \rightarrow \mathrm{F}x)$,' which can be decided a priori. And those lawlike statements that are accepted because they are fertile although they have no truth value (e.g., the normative metanomological statements) will then be counted as metascientific. A third, not so obvious, requisite is *systemicity* or incorporation in some theory, however rudimentary it be. Systemicity will automatically take care of an important property that distinguishes law statements from daily life generalizations: namely, the occurrence of at least one specific non-commonsensical, or technical, term. This condition will rule out from the class of laws general and even true sentences like "Apes dislike snakes."

Further requisites that are sometimes imposed—such as necessity, causality, plausibility, counterfactual force, inductive character, and simplicity—seem unnecessary and even mutilating. (Simplicity should be invoked only for minor surgical purposes, such as extruding irrelevant information and tautologies.) The three requisites above are sufficient to decide that, say, "Pottery is fragile" and "Crows are black" are nonlaw statements; they are universal and well corroborated, but they lack systemicity. Yet, such stray true *LLS* may some day be deduced from law statements.

We are then left with but three requisites: generality in some

[8] The qualification 'genuine' is intended to exclude—certainly in an imprecise way—pseudouniversal statements of the form '$(x)(x = a \rightarrow Fx)$.'

respect, empirical corroboration, and systemicity. But, since generality is a property of the genus *LLS,* only corroboration and systemicity remain as traits peculiar to law statements and, consequently—at the pragmatic level—as criteria of lawfulness. This suggests proposing the following linguistic convention as a *liberal criterion of lawfulness: A proposition is a law statement if and only if it is general in some respect (i.e. does not refer to unique objects), has been empirically corroborated in some domain in a satisfactory way (for the time being), and belongs to some theory (whether adult or embryonic).*

## 6. *Conclusion*

It is for scientists to say whether the above elucidation of the concept of scientific law conforms in a satisfactory way with actual usage, i.e., whether the intension matches the extension. If it were adopted, its upshot for the theory of science could be summed up in the following way. Science as a product of research is a web of propositions and proposals; some are formal (linguistic, logical, and mathematical) and others are factual (they have extralinguistic referents and depend upon them for their truth or their efficiency). Factual statements may be classified as scientific hypotheses (with varying degrees of validation), nonlinguistic conventions, rules or norms of procedure (with varying degrees of conduciveness), and criteria or desiderata. Hypotheses (corrigible statements) range from the humblest observation reports to the most sweeping and deepest lawlike statements; they may, in fact, be divided into informations and lawlike statements. The subclass of corroborated and systemic lawlike statements we decide to call law statements.

There are as many classifications of law statements as viewpoints can profitably be adopted in their regard, and there seems to be no reason—save for certain philosophical traditions—why most law statements should be regarded as nonlaw statements merely because they fail to comply either with certainty, or strict universality, or causality, or simplicity, or any other requisite found desirable in the past, when science seemed concerned exclusively with white swans and falling bodies. Criteria of laws have changed because new kinds of law—or, if preferred, new usages of the term 'law'—have been set up, particularly since the birth of the sciences of man. That lawlike statements require corroboration and systemicity in order to be ranked as law statements seems to fit contemporary usage in the sciences. By adopting it we get into the bargain the probable stimulus that workers in the sciences of man may be led to seek further regularities (not necessarily as universal as the law of gravitation), and to invent theoretical models that may account for them—which they will shy away from if they are told that law statements, the real ones, are the privilege of theoretical physics.

# 11

# Causality, Chance, and Law

The causal principle fell into disrepute during the first half of our century as an effect of two independent events: the criticisms of empiricist and conventionalist philosophers, and the growing use in science and technology of statistical ideas and methods. Progress in knowledge was, at one point, viewed as taking place in three stages. In the first stage, spirits were replaced by causes (or, if preferred, animism by Aristotelianism). In the second stage, causes were replaced by forces (mechanism replaced Aristotelianism). And in the third and last stage, forces were replaced by laws (a noncommittal world outlook replaced mechanism). But this picture of the progress of knowledge has proved to be an oversimplification.

In fact, superstitious persons have often conceived of spirits as causes and even as capable of exerting forces on physical objects: witness the belief in psychokinesis. And we realize that forces are a kind of cause and are subject to law (whenever they are not armed), so that the concepts of cause, force, and law, are far from being mutually exclusive. We also grant that laws may be causal or noncausal and, in particular, that chance is not the absence of law but the outcome of lawful process and is, in turn, subject to laws of a higher order (statistical regularities).

We have renounced spirits, but not causes and forces on condition that they be law-abiding. We retain the concepts of cause and force in their proper contexts, namely, philosophy and dynamics respectively. But we do not regard cause and force as panaceas for the explanation of becoming: we account for change in terms of laws that may or may not involve the concepts of cause and force. Contemporary science has not expelled causes and forces in the name of law: it has subjected the former to the latter and has assigned both strict causation and force narrower but still important domains.

The realization of the statistical nature of all macroscopic laws, and of the objective nature of chance, has not led us to believe in uncaused events: it has only shown that not all relations are causal bonds. We grant that the sequence of fire outbreaks and suicides in a city are random, but this does not prevent the insurance companies from thoroughly inquiring into the causes of every single fire and suicide. And an analysis of such causes, if deep enough, will involve certain laws of nature or society, some with a causal ingredient, others predominantly statistical.

Causation, chance, and law are intertwined in most scientific analyses of matters of fact as long as these are not restricted to a description of appearances. The following should bear out this statement.

## 1. *The Causal Relation*

Causation has traditionally been understood as the constant and one-one relation among events whereby causes produce effects. Accordingly the causal principle may be stated thus:[1] *If C happens, then (and only then) E is always produced by it.* This formula states neither a constant *conjunction* nor a constant *succession* of events: the gist of causation is uniform *production* rather than mere coincidence or following in order. Let us illustrate this interpretation with some examples.

Some psychophysiologists believe that thought processes are *accompanied* by synchronous physiological processes but not *produced* by the latter, either because they hold the simple hypothesis of parallelism (as is the case of C. Sherrington), or because they think psychological phenomena are physiological phenomena "seen" from within, i.e., regarded subjectively (e.g., A. Lipshutz). And we say that infancy is *followed* by youth, not that the former *produces* the latter. Conjunction and succession may be external to each other and even accidental, which is not the case of production.

On the other hand, we do not say that demoralization happens to be merely conjoined with, or to follow upon, unemployment: we believe there is a specific psychosocial mechanism whereby moral derangement is *produced* by inactivity and social estrangement, just as we believe heavy rains produce erosion and tranquilizers produce relaxation. That not every production of an effect is *causal,* that is, that not every effect is related to its causes in the simple way stated by the causal principle, is another matter.

What produces and what is produced are always *events,* that is, changes in the state of real entities, whether natural or cultural. Hence, a necessary, though not sufficient, condition for a law to be causal is that it relates *differences* of some sort and,

[1] M. Bunge, *Causality: The Place of the Causal Principle in Modern Science* (Cambridge, Mass.: Harvard University Press, 1959).

more precisely, differences in the properties that specify the states of a concrete system.

The temperature and available energy of a physical system are functionally related, and so are the price and mean life of a merchandise, but such relations are noncausal. Properties, or even sets of properties (states), cannot produce other properties: it is only a *change* $\Delta P$ in the cluster of properties $P$ that may *produce* a change $\Delta Q$ in a related system of properties $Q$. Even so, the two changes may not be *causally* related: they may be concomitant or successive, without the one producing the other. Hence not every constant relation among properties, not even every constant relation among variations of properties, is a causal law.

Consider, for instance, Boyle's law $pV = \text{const}$. It certainly expresses a constant relation between two key properties of an ideal model of a certain class of entities (gases). But it is not a *causal* relation although we can rephrase it in terms of variations of properties, i.e. in terms of events. In fact, upon differentiation we obtain $dp \cdot V + V \cdot dp = 0$, whence

$$\frac{-dV}{V} = \frac{dp}{p} \qquad (\textit{Compression} = \textit{Pressurization}) \qquad (1)$$

Recalling the obvious rules of meaning of the symbols involved, this equation may be read as follows: The relative decrease in volume equals the relative increase in pressure that *accompanies* the compression. Notice the symmetry of this statement; it suggests no arrow indicating a one-sided relation between a cause and an effect, it does not allow us to tell which is which. Even more to the point: compression and pressurization are two traits of one and *the same* event—a change of state of the gaseous system. And an event cannot be causally related to itself, by the definition of causation.

However, and this is overlooked by functionalism,[2] a causal

[2] For a recent account and defense of the functionalist view of causation see, e.g., F. Waismann, "The Decline and Fall of Causality," in A. C. Crombie *et al., Turning Points in Physics* (New York: Harper & Brothers, 1961), p. 87.

statement can be obtained from the above if the environment of the physical system is taken into account. By so doing we may be able to point to an externally impressed force as the *cause* of the compression and the simultaneous increase in internal pressure. And we are bound to take this more comprehensive view if we wish to understand the *origin* of change in addition to recording and summarizing it.

Furthermore, we may look into this same event with the help of a deeper theory, the kinetic theory of matter, which will tell us what the "external" or phenomenological theory will not—namely, that a compression will *produce* an increase in internal pressure because less space will be available for the motion of the molecules, the increased number of impacts of which on the walls of the container is macroscopically manifested as an increased pressure.

The description of an event or process as causal or as noncausal will depend on the context in which the description is made and, in particular, on the laws involved in that description. And the laws occurring in it will in turn depend on the level of analysis and on the knowledge at hand. Nothing is *inherently* causal or noncausal. The question "Is *x* causal?" should always be completed in some such way as "Is *x* causal relative to the bundle of law statements *L*?"

## 2. *The Causal Range of a Law*

The description of an event or process by means of a set of laws and a set of informations concerning actual circumstances can be said to be causal if certain conditions are jointly satisfied. It may be argued [3] that the following conditions are jointly necessary and sufficient:

(*a*) The system concerned and its environment are fairly *distinct* from one another; in pragmatic terms, an inside and an outside can be clearly recognized.

[3] For a slightly different set of conditions and an argument in favor of their relevance, see my *Causality* (fn. 1), 13.2.1.

(*b*) The main changes under consideration are produced by *external* factors; the internal determinants, which give rise to the so-called spontaneous (but lawful) behavior and are always present, are negligible in the respect that is being investigated and to the approximation that has been agreed upon.

(*c*) The process in question, involving both the system and its environment, can be regarded as practically *isolated,* i.e., its actual connections with the rest of the world are practically ignorable; in particular, it is possible to neglect the random perturbations that are constantly impinging upon any real system.

(*d*) Every interaction can be approximated by *one-sided* agent-patient relations; i.e., the reactions of the system upon its environment can be neglected.

(*e*) The input and the output can be related in a *one-one* way to each other, with neglect of both multiple causation and statistical relations between sets of causes and sets of effects.

If the above conditions are not fulfilled we may still have a perfectly *determinate* description—corresponding to a determinate event—but not a *causal* one. Now, the above conditions are difficult if not impossible to meet in actual fact. Therefore *strictly* causal laws are never exactly operating. There is always, as a matter of fact, some amount of spontaneity, mutual action, and randomness. In other words, there are no purely causal laws. There are, rather, *causal ranges* of scientific laws, or domains in which certain laws of nature or society are *predominantly* causal, at least at some level of analysis. Let me introduce the notion of causal range with the help of an illustration.

Suppose we are interested in behavior. Let our fundamental variables be the strength $S_e$ of the external stimuli, the strength $S_i$ of the internal stimuli, the overt or external response $R_e$, and the covert or inner response $R_i$. The total response $R = R_e + R_i$ will be a (still unknown) function $F$ of the remaining variables:

$$R_e + R_i = F(S_e, S_i) \qquad (2)$$

Now, below the so-called absolute threshold—i.e., below a certain value of the stimulus—there is no response; since there is input but no output, there is no causal relation in this interval. Let this be called a *noncausal range* of the law schema (2).

A further noncausal feature of (2) is the occurrence in it of the inner stimuli $S_i$. In the first place, this factor is not external to the system (organism), as it should if it were to be called a cause in agreement with clause (*b*) above. Secondly, the internal stimuli and the total response $R$ are nothing but different *aspects* of one and the same functioning of the organism. Thirdly, since the internal stimuli give rise to "spontaneous" responses—i.e., to responses that are not elicited by the external, controllable stimuli—the function $F$ in (2) includes a random variable, i.e., a variable unrelated to $S_e$, but presumably related to subbehavioral, physiological parameters.[4]

Hence, if we wish to obtain the causal range of the law schema (2) we have to neglect the internal stimuli or hold them constant (which is only approximately possible), so as to be sure that only external factors will produce behavior effects. In this approximation equation (2) becomes

$$R_e + R_i = G(S_e), \tag{3}$$

where '$G$' designates a new function. If we further neglect the covert responses, which for the time being are inscrutable in the case of nonhuman subjects anyhow, we obtain the famous psychophysical law

$$R_e = k \cdot S_e^p, \tag{4}$$

where $p = 0.3$ for sound.

We may call equations (3) and (4) *causal approximations* of equation (2). We may also say that the *causal range* of the law schema (2) is the region for which the internal stimuli $S_i$ are negligible as compared with the external stimuli (i.e., $S_i \ll S_e$).

Similar results may be obtained in other fields; in science we always deal with concrete systems presumably having an internal

[4] This conjecture is explored and discussed in M. Bunge, "*Causality: A Rejoinder*," *Philosophy of Science, 29,* 306 (1962).

structure and interacting with a part of their environment, and the study of such systems and their changes (events and strings of events) can be made on various levels of analysis and, consequently, with various degrees of approximation. Sometimes the approximations or simplifications are such that *causal interpretations* of the laws are possible and desirable. But every causal interpretation, if adequate at all, is only approximately valid. As soon as a deeper analysis is performed, further, noncausal, categories of determination—such as statistical determination, teleological determination, dialectical determination, and so on—will occur. Let us sketch a program for such a deeper analysis in the case of behavior.

The general psychophysical relation (2) is *phenomenological* or nonrepresentational, in the sense that it involves no "mechanism" connecting the several variables. Although equation (2) has a causal range, it is phenomenological because it treats the organism as a "black box" upon which stimuli impinge and out of which responses emerge. On the other hand a deeper, representational, theory of behavior will take the risk of proposing definite "mechanisms" linking (*a*) the external stimuli to the responses, and (*b*) the physiological and psychological levels.

Conceivably such deeper, representational or nonphenomenological, theories of behavior would depart from causality even more than the phenomenological theory. They would account not only for the randomly impinging external stimuli and the internal stimuli of various sorts, but they would also postulate *inter-level relations,* which are noncausal.

One such inter-level or border-zone law, linking properties belonging to different levels of organization of one and the same organism, would be the relation between the internal stimuli $S_i$ (such as hunger and other drives) and the underlying physiological variables $\phi$ (such as sugar level in blood). Representational or neodeterministic theories of behavior would provide, then, equations of the form

$$R_e + R_i = H[S_e, S_i(\phi), \phi]. \tag{5}$$

It should be clear that the relation $S_i = S_i(\phi)$ between the set of physiological variables $\phi$ and the psychological variables $S_i$ is not a *causal* relation, no matter how precise it is and no matter how accurately it would enable us to predict behavior with the help of physiological information. There is no question here of an unsymmetrical relation of production between an external "agent" and an internal "patient," but only a relation between two levels of one and the same organism. (For an elucidation of the level concept, see Chapter 3.)

The internal stimulus $S_i$ is a whole compounded of micro-changes described by the physiological variables we have lumped in $\phi$. Such a noncausal relation is not a mere "reduction," since nothing is explained *away* by positing the relation $S_i = S_i(\phi)$. Neither is $S_i$ eliminated in favor of $\phi$, nor is $\phi$ reduced to $S_i$: the two variables describe peculiar traits of an organism at different levels, and the fact that its behavior might partially, or even totally, be explained by reference to lower-level processes does not annihilate behavior as such. Logical reduction (explanation) need not involve ontological reduction (levelling), just as the disclosure of a deeper level may, but need not, involve the disclosure of causes.

In short, 'causal' is a qualifier that can best be applied to laws of a certain kind when certain rather stringent conditions are approximately met. As a consequence, in the absence of knowledge of the pertinent laws and circumstances it does not make much sense to ask whether a given event or process is causal. This does not mean that causation is a wholly subjective category; but it does imply that the use of the term 'causal' in technical contexts should not be unruly.

Let us now turn to the examination of the persistent confusions between causation, the temporal precedence of the cause over the effect, and the continuity of causal lines.

### 3. *Causality, Antecedence, and Contiguity*

Local field physics has accustomed us to such an extent to the union of causation, antecedence, and nearby action, that we often fail to recognize that these principles are *logically* independent of one another no matter how closely they may hang together in most of contemporary physics. Yet such a logical independence must be granted in order to understand the mere existence of causal thought before and outside field physics, and also in order to leave the door open to the possible relaxation of the condition of contiguity or nearby action in favor of so-called nonlocal interactions.

The confusion between antecedence and causation is so common that philosophers have found it necessary, very long ago, to coin a special phrase to brand this fallacy, namely, *Post hoc, ergo propter hoc* (after that, hence because of that). It is not physically possible for the effect to precede its cause, since the cause is supposed to give rise to, or to produce, or to contribute to the production of the effect, e.g., by means of an energy transfer. But it would be logically possible for the cause and the effect to be simultaneous in a given frame of reference, particularly if they occurred at the same place. Even if the cause and the effect took place at different regions in space, one could imagine that a physical agent might traverse a distance in no time—as has been held by most theories of action at a distance. And such an instantaneous action at a distance would be perfectly compatible with causality—Hume and Humeans notwithstanding.[5]

All that the *principle of antecedence* states is that the cause cannot happen *after* the effect. This excludes, among other conceivable phenomena, so-called precognition, claimed by believers in ESP, since what does not yet exist cannot be a source of information (or even of noise) for what exists. A possible general formulation of the principle of antecedence is this: *B at time t is uniquely determined by A at all times t′ prior to and up to t*. In obvious symbols, $A(t' \leq t)\ D\ B(t)$.

Unlike the principle of causation, the principle of antecedence can be given a precise mathematical formulation. Let $K(t', t)$ be the strength of the contribution of the antecedent

[5] See fn. 1, Chapter 3.

$A(t')$ at time $t'$; this contribution will usually depend on the lapse $t'$-$t$ and, more often than not, it will fade out rapidly with increasing time intervals. Then the contribution of $A$ to the consequent $B$ during the time interval $dt'$ will be $K_1(t', t) \cdot A(t') \cdot dt'$, and the total effect $B$ at time $t$ will be obtained by collecting all the contributions of $A$ at previous times, i.e., by summing them:

$$B(t) = \int_{-\infty}^{t} K_1(t', t) \cdot A(t') \cdot dt' \quad (\textit{Antecedence}) \tag{6}$$

In most cases the past history of the system will be short or it will be entirely incorporated in the immediately prior state of the system; but in a few cases the system will have a memory of some sort, i.e., after-effects will occur. Mathematically, the memory function $K_1(t', t)$ will in a few cases differ from 0 over an interval. If $A$ operates only at time $t$, or if the system has no memory, the contribution of $A$ will be represented by an impulsive "function": $K_1(t', t) = k\,\delta\,(t' - t)$, whence $B(t) = k\,A(t)$.

In any case, the antecedent $A$ and the consequent $B$ are not necessarily connected in a causal way according to equation (6). In fact, the principle of antecedence does not speak about the antecedent $A$ *producing* the consequent $B$, but about $B$ being both *dependent* upon and *following* $A$, or being at most simultaneous with $A$. '$A$' and '$B$' will usually designate properties or states (clusters of properties) rather than events. Furthermore, no reference to an external action of $A$ upon a system is made in (6). In short, antecedence is compatible with causality but logically independent of it.

As to the principle of *nearby action,* or contiguity, it states that whatever happens at some place is the effect of what happens in its neighborhood. The latter is not limited to immediate vicinity; conditions in distant regions (reported in the so-called boundary conditions) are usually as important as conditions in the immediate neighborhood. The principle of contiguity would be falsified if something could jump over space without travelling through it. If there are trajectories, the principle requires that they be continuous; but it does not require that the velocities along such trajectories (continuous as well) be finite. In other words, the principle of nearby action does not exclude the possibility of instantaneous propagation. The existence of limiting velocities (or velocity) must be postulated independently of both the principle of contiguity and the principle of antecedence.

A possible general formulation of the principle of nearby action is this: *$B$ at the place $x$ is uniquely determined by $A$ at the places $x'$ surrounding $x$.* In symbols, $A(x' \neq x)\ D\ B(x)$. To be more specific, let $K_2(x', x)$ be the weight of the factor $A$ at the point $x'$; this contribution will usually depend on the distance $x' - x$ between $x'$ and $x$, and it will usually decrease with increasing distance. The contribution of $A$ to $B$ over the volume element $dx'$ will be $K_2(x', x) \cdot A(x') \cdot dx'$ and the total effect of $A$ at $x$ will be obtained by scanning the whole space and collecting all the local contributions, i.e.,

$$B(x) = \int_{-\infty}^{\infty} K_2(x', x) \cdot A(x') \cdot dx' \quad \textit{(Nearby action)} \qquad (7)$$

Notice the analogy between the mathematical formulations of the principles of contiguity (7) and antecedence (6). But note also the difference: while we collect contributions from left and right (actually, from all over a three-dimensional manifold), we stop collecting contributions at time $t$, and this simply because there *is* nothing to collect from a still unborn time. Time is the pace, not the source, of becoming.

These two principles may be regarded as particular cases of a third principle, which might be called the *principle of spacetime contiguity*. The form of this principle is, obviously,

$$A(x' \neq x, t' \leq t)\ DB(x, t)$$

A possible general formulation of this hypothesis in quantitative terms is

$$B(x, t) = \int_{-\infty}^{t} dt' \int_{-\infty}^{\infty} dx' \cdot K(t', t; x', x) \cdot A(x', t') \quad \textit{(Spacetime contiguity)} \qquad (8)$$

If the postulate of the upper velocity of propagation of physical disturbances is added, the space integration will be restricted by the condition $|x' - x| \leq c|t' - t|$. Putting

$$K = \delta(x' - x) \cdot K_1(t', t)$$

we obtain the principle of antecedence (6), which can then be interpreted—in this wider context—as spacetime contiguity when the antecedent and the consequent are located in the same place. And putting

$$K = \delta(t' - t) \cdot K_2(x', x)$$

we obtain the principle of nearby action in its special form (7). There still is no causality, although many a physicist would like to call equation (8) a "causality condition."

In contemporary field physics the so-called *strict local causality* "condition" (that is, hypothesis) is usually respected. This assumption, which bears such an unfortunate name, can be read as follows: Parts of a field that cannot be connected by a field ripple (a light wave in the case of the electromagnetic field) cannot interact. A corollary of this objective physical law statement is the following nomopragmatic statement:[6] The measurement of a field variable at any given point in spacetime will not affect the measurement of the same (let alone of a different) field quantity in a place that cannot be reached from the former by a field signal.

"Strict local causality" is a misnomer for the above principle, which is nothing but a specification of the principle of space-

[6] The term 'nomopragmatic statement' stands for a law statement cast in a way convenient for validation or use. See M. Bunge, *Metascientific Queries* (Springfield, Ill.: Charles C. Thomas, Publisher, 1959), Chapter 4. Since in the quantum theory of fields the field variables are operators instead of numerical variables, the so-called "causality condition" cannot be expressed by a formula like (8). Usual statements of the "causality condition" are commutation relations among the field variables $\psi_i(x)$ at different points $x$, and $x'$, of spacetime, such as, e.g.,

$$\psi_i(x)\psi_k(x') - \psi_k(x')\psi_i(x) = i \cdot \delta_{ik} \cdot \Delta(x - x')$$

time contiguity. In fact, the field variables the principle ties up are supposed to undergo spontaneous random fluctuations, and randomness—particularly if uncaused—is not precisely compatible with causality at one and the same level. Incidentally, the mere occurrence of postulates such as the "causality condition" shows once more that the quantum theory is *not indeterministic,* no matter how uncausal it may be. In fact, the theory does not hold that anything may happen but, on the contrary, it "prohibits" such logically conceivable events as the interaction of field regions not connectible by a field disturbance (mathematically: separated by a spacelike interval).

In short, antecedence and contiguity, while *compatible* with causality, are not entailed by it. For one thing, the principles of antecedence and contiguity refer to properties (denoted by variables) rather than to events. Secondly, these variables may be "classical" quantities, probability amplitudes, or random variables—i.e., variables with built-in chance, so to say. On the other hand, the changes of properties involved in the causal principle are not supposed to be subject to random fluctuations. Thirdly, there exists no general mathematical formulation of the causal principle, whereas both antecedence and contiguity can be given fairly general mathematical expressions, as witnessed by equations (6) to (8).

While it is important to realize the differences between causation and spacetime contiguity, it is no less important to recognize that antecedence and contiguity, combined with specific assumptions (laws) concerning particle motion and field structure, do provide specific *mechanisms* of physical determination. Such mechanisms may have a causal ingredient (as occurs with the assumption that the acceleration of masses and charges produce waves) even though they may make room for a noncausal process, such as the self-sustained propagation of a wave in a void.

Moreover, chance itself is often traceable to the operation of mechanisms. To this we now turn.

## 4. *Causality and Chance*

Causation and chance are often regarded as polar concepts, and not without some reason—as long as it is not forgotten that bulky masses of chance events may average out to nearly "causal lines" and that, vice versa, the interplay of numerous nearly independent and individually determinate entities results always in chaotic situations.

For example, the motion of a single particle in a smoke stream is like the almost-random walk of a drunkard; yet the stream as a whole has a well-defined geometrical and dynamical pattern, even when it degenerates into a collection of small vortex motions. Conversely, every single marriage is supposed to be the outcome of a planned course of action, yet the sequence of marriages in a community is a random sequence in time. Random behavior at the microscopic individual level may result in ordered behavior at a macroscopic collective level, and orderly individual behavior may fit a random collective pattern. Moreover, chance has its peculiar laws. Thus smoke particles and drunkards will move away from a given point to an average distance proportional to the square root of the time elapsed, and the average age of brides will be a fairly constant characteristic of every community.

There is nothing arbitrary in chance. Consider, for instance, a simplified roulette game in which only "reds" and "blacks" occur. Poincaré[7] proved that, no matter what the initial positions and velocities of the marbles may be in the successive trials, the long-run frequency of "reds" and "blacks" will be the same, namely, $\frac{1}{2}$. In other words, any initial distribution will ensue, in the long run, in a fixed, perfectly determinate, final distribution. This phenomenon, described by means of what is known as the method of arbitrary functions, is not arbitrary itself—a nice example of the absence of one-one correspondence

[7] H. Poincaré, *Calcul des Probabilités*, 2nd ed. (Paris: Gauthier-Villars, 1912), pp. 148 ff.

between facts and constructs. Far from being arbitrary, the mechanism of the phenomenon is stable in the sense that, no matter how we vary the circumstances (in this case the initial conditions), provided we do it without bias, the outcome is always the same in the long run. In this respect, chance phenomena do not differ from more strongly determinate phenomena: in either case we have invariable *laws* holding for variable individuals in variable circumstances. What characterizes chance is not the absence of law but the lack of sensitivity to detail.

Disorder, far from being absolute, is relative to a set of laws. Killing, a disorderly behavior in civilized society, becomes orderly behavior in war. The assertion "The $x$'s are random, accidental, or contingent" is as misleading as "The $x$'s are causal." On the other hand, a relativized assertion such as "The $x$'s are accidental relative to the bundle of law statements $L$" is not only meaningful but also testable as soon as a large set of similar $x$'s can be examined and the bundle of laws is specified. Even though the $x$'s in question may be accidental with respect to the laws $L$, they may not be accidental relative to a different bundle, $L'$, of laws. That is, both $-Lx$ and $L'x$ may be true for a given value of $x$. (For example, every single accidental error of measurement fits the bell-shaped distribution curve.) In short, chance is not absolute but is relative to law .

Quite often, the predication of chance is the result of a limited view. For instance, the differences in the initial positions and velocities of the marble in the roulette game are, in turn, the outcome of individually orderly (but not controlled) processes; they do not spring out of nothing, they do not violate what may be called the genetic principle. It is only by deciding, for *practical* reasons, to ignore their past histories that we are lured into talking of *chaotic* initial conditions or distributions. Again, storms and other meteorological phenomena are random if regarded, so to speak, from the outside; but modern, dynamic meteorology is disclosing the mechanism of storms and is in principle capable of predicting every single storm. The random nature of the whole sequence of storms will not thereby disappear: it will merely by explained; and the explanation will be performed in terms of laws of averages (fluid dynamics and thermodynamics). The explanation of chance does not eliminate it.

Any perfectly definite mechanism involving a large number of nearly independent (i.e., weakly interacting) similar entities, whether they be electrons or humans, will produce a stable limiting frequency of some sort or other. For example, an initially heterogeneous distribution of dust particles in the air will, in the long run and annoyingly enough, become quite uniformly distributed on the floor and furniture.

Chance is not chaos or lawlessness. Far from being arbitrary, every chance distribution is characterized by certain constant frequencies, averages, and mean fluctuations—whence pure chance is so difficult to imitate. Thus we will hesitate to say that the $n$-th decimal figure of the logarithms of positive integers are randomly distributed, unless we can ascertain that every digit occurs in that $n$-th place with nearly the same frequency 1/10—as in fact it does. We speak of randomness if and only if individual irregularities build up collective (statistical) regularities.

Any detailed description of random processes will involve the concepts of law, circumstance (e.g., initial conditions), and probability. The occurrence of the term 'probability' will not, of course, be designed to mask our ignorance. On the contrary, we can make use of probability theory only if we know or assume something concerning the system—for instance, laws of motion, symmetry properties, or almost stable frequencies. The probability distributions occurring in factual science are not a product of human frailty but an achievement of research. Moreover, such distributions are supposed to mirror objective traits of the world. The fact that ignorance of certain details is involved in the statement of many probability problems shows not that ignorance generates chance, but that knowledge of the same details would not alter the result.

Chance and causation are probably as much objective traits of the world as any conceptual model can be. Perfect randomness is perhaps almost as much of an abstraction as perfect causation is, and yet neither is in our minds *alone*. We infer that the world has a causal ingredient because we establish some laws that have a causal approximation, just as we infer that the world is made up of chance as well, because we find some statistical laws to work.[8]

### 5. *Inferring Causation from Correlation*

From complete randomness to strict causation there is a continuum of degrees of correlation. This correlation is measurable, and is helpful in the search for systematic relations, such as causal bonds. Suppose we wish to find out whether the factors or variables $x$ and $y$ (or, rather, their variations) are systematically related to one another. (By 'systematic relation' I mean what is usually, and wrongly, called causal relation—i.e., 'systematic relation' covers functional relation, interaction, and causation.) Suppose further that we are prevented from either observing $x$ and $y$ or varying them at will, say, because they represent social traits such as urbanization and technical skill.

Obviously two cases are possible: either $x$ is systematically related to $y$, in which case we write $xSy$, or $x$ is not systematically related to $y$, a situation we symbolize $x\bar{S}y$. In the first case the absolute value of the coefficient of correlation, $r_{xy}$, will be near 1; in the second case it will be approximately 0. In short, we have the two conditionals

$$\text{If } xSy, \text{ then } r_{xy} \cong 1.$$
$$\text{If } x\bar{S}y, \text{ then } r_{xy} \cong 0.$$

We now gather data and compute $r_{xy}$. If the empirically found value of $r_{xy}$ is near 1, we infer that $xSy$, and if it is near 0 we

[8] An early recognition of the objectivity of chance is found in F. Exner, *Vorlesungen über die physikalischen Grundlagen der Naturwissenschaften* (Leipzig und Wien: Deuticke, 1922). But Exner opposed chance to lawfulness and equated the latter with causality. For an independent enquiry into the category of chance as an objective mode of behavior, see M. Bunge, "What Is Chance?," *Science & Society*, 15 (1951), 209. See also D. Bohm, *Causality and Chance in Modern Physics* (London: Routledge & Kegan Paul, 1957).

infer that $x\bar{S}y$. But, of course, either inference is at best plausible, because all we know is the converse of the first conditional, namely, that *if* there is a systematic relation between $x$ and $y$, it is likely to show up in a high correlation. The converse is not true: a high correlation will *suggest* but will not *establish* a systematic relation.

Contrary to usage, we have been speaking of a *systematic* rather than of a *causal* relation between $x$ and $y$. The reason is this: a high value of the coefficient of correlation $r_{xy}$ is compatible with at least the following different hypotheses concerning the nature of the relation tying $x$ to $y$: (*a*) $x$ and $y$ are *functionally* related to one another, such as $p$ and $V$ in Boyle's law; (*b*) $x$ and $y$ are *interacting* factors, and indeed mutually favorable ones, such as rainfall and vegetation; (*c*) $x$ *causes* $y$; (*d*) $y$ *causes* $x$; (*e*) $x$ and $y$ are both produced by a third factor $z$. The frequent *conjunction* of $x$ and $y$, or the concomitance of their variations, as indicated by a high value of $r_{xy}$, does not establish their *causal* relation. And scientists—unlike Humean philosophers—are vitally interested in the difference between a frequent conjunction and a uniform production.

To make a decision among the various hypotheses with the finding $r_{xy} \cong 1$, additional information, analyses, and criteria are needed. Some of the criteria used in physics are: (*a*) $y$ comes after $x$; (*b*) $y$ is near $x$; (*c*) $y$ is more stable than $x$; (*d*) $y$ is associated with a greater entropy than $x$ is; (*e*) $y$ is associated with a smaller potential energy (or else free energy) than $x$ is. However, none of these criteria could by itself more than *support* the hypothesis that $x$ causes $y$. Only a detailed study, both empirical and theoretical, of the relation between $x$ and $y$—a study going far beyond the statistical data at hand, and deeply into the mechanism involved—might eventually establish that $x$ and $y$ are parts of a causal process.

In short, by itself the statistical method cannot establish the existence of causal relations, although it can suggest the existence of a mechanism which may be partly causal. This conclusion is reinforced by a study of statistical correlation among more than two variables. If for two variables we had two possible causal hypotheses, "$x \rightarrow y$" and "$y \rightarrow x$," for three variables we have no less than a dozen causal hypotheses—not to count the noncausal ones. In fact, if there is a systematic relation among the three variables $x$, $y$, and $z$, in addition to the functional relations $z = f(x, y)$ and the interaction $x \leftrightarrow y \leftrightarrow z$, we have the following possible models:

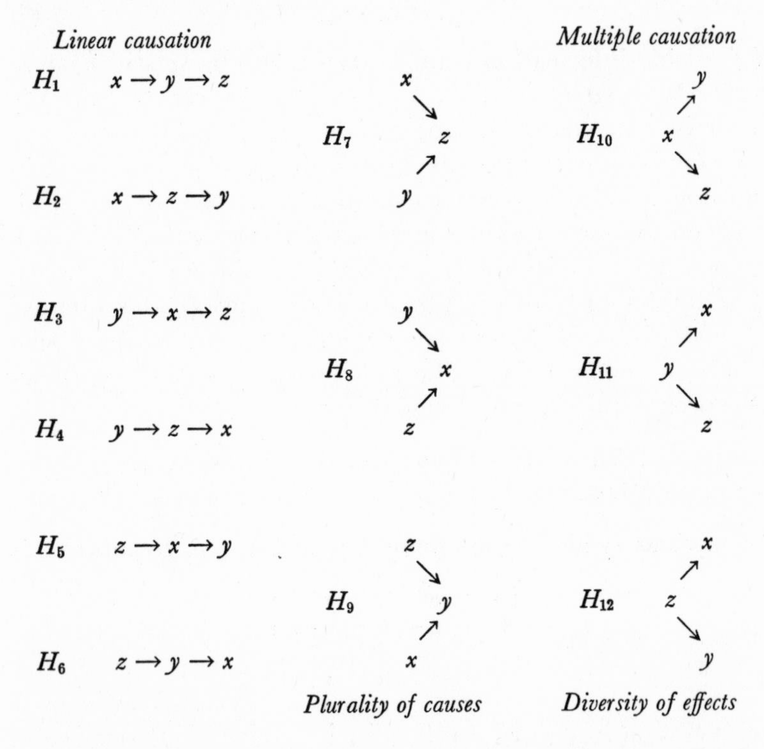


All such cases, where some variables are indirectly related—as $x$ and $z$ in "$x \rightarrow y \rightarrow z$"—come under the heading of the so-called spurious correlation; the variable mediating between the extremes is often called the intervening variable. In multiple causation with a plurality of causes and a single effect (hypotheses $H_7$ to $H_9$), the causes may be jointly or disjointly operative, and in either case their coefficient of correlation may be nearly zero. In all other cases interesting relations can be established among the indirectly related variables and, by making further assumptions of a nonstatistical character, inferences can be drawn about likely systematic patterns of relations (some of which may be causal).[9] For example, for both $H_1$ and $H_{11}$ we have

$$r_{xz} = r_{xy} \cdot r_{yz}. \qquad (9)$$

If available information confirms this relation, we still have to decide between $H_1$ and $H_{11}$. The ambiguity can be partially or totally removed by making certain specific assumptions.

Sociologists and anthropologists are, of course, interested in knowing whether a given set of social variables, or traits, all stand on the same footing or are somehow genetically related. Suppose we consider the interrelations of the following variables: division of labor ($w$), prenuptial residence ($x$), land tenure ($y$), and system of descent ($z$), all with reference to the North American Indian tribes. The following competing hypotheses have been put to the test of statistics:[10]

$H_1$ $\quad w \rightarrow x \;\&\; x \rightarrow y \;\&\; y \rightarrow z$

$H_2$ $\quad w \rightarrow x \;\&\; w \rightarrow y \;\&\; x \rightarrow y \;\&\; y \rightarrow z$

An obvious symbolic representation of the two hypotheses is

$H_1$ $\quad$ *w* *x* *y* *z*<br>
o → o → o → o

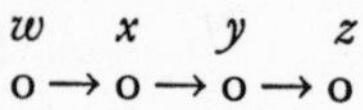

*w* *x*<br>
o → o<br>
$H_2$ $\quad$ ↘ ↓<br>
o ← o<br>
*z* *y*

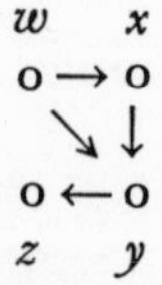

[9] See H. A. Simon, "Spurious Correlation: A Causal Interpretation," *Journal of the American Statistical Association,* 49 (1954), 467, and H. M. Blalock, "Correlational Analysis and Causal Inference," *American Anthropologist,* 62 (1960), 624.

[10] See Blalock, *op. cit.*

According to equation (9), if $H_1$ is true, we should find the following predictions to be confirmed:

$$\begin{array}{ll} P_{11} & r_{wy} = r_{wx} \cdot r_{xy} \\ P_{12} & r_{xz} = r_{xy} \cdot r_{yz} \\ P_{13} & r_{wz} = r_{wx} \cdot r_{xy} \cdot r_{yz} \end{array} \tag{10}$$

On the other hand, on the basis of $H_2$ and equation (9) we should predict the following statistical relations:

$$\begin{array}{ll} P_{21} & r_{xz} = r_{xy} \cdot r_{yz} \\ P_{22} & r_{wz} = r_{wy} \cdot r_{yz} \end{array} \tag{11}$$

Notice, in the first place, that $H_1$ is simpler than $H_2$ but has more complex consequences than $H_2$. Note, in the second place, that predictions $P_{12}$ and $P_{21}$ are identical but the remaining predictions are quite different. Hence a clear-cut decision between the two rival hypotheses, or against both of them, is possible on the basis of empirical data.

It so happened that data supported the second hypothesis, which had been advanced prior to the test. But the same data support also alternative hypotheses, such as those obtained by reversing some or even all of the arrows in $H_2$. However, the anthropologist will adduce further laws, or further data, to show that such reversals are unlikely or even impossible.

In conclusion, statistics, far from being the grave of causality, is a tool that may suggest the existence of systematic relations and, in particular, of causal relations. The inference of causal laws from statistical regularities is not unambiguous, but the ambiguity can sometimes be reduced or even removed with the help of additional information and assumptions of a nonstatistical nature. Once again, randomness in some respect is compatible with causality in another respect, and each is subject to law.

### 6. *Causality, Lawfulness, and Determinism*

The existing variety of kinds of scientific law, as exhibited in Chapter 10 (see especially section 4), shows how misleading the equation *Causality* = *Lawfulness* is, despite the fact that it enjoys the authority of both Aristotle and Hume, not to count philosophically naive scientists.

Equally confusing is the equation *Determinism* = *Causality*, once the multiplicity of kinds of *determiners*—noncausal and causal—has been recognized, i.e., once it has been realized that things can acquire, retain, and lose properties in a variety of ways. For, after all, when we say that *x determines y* we mean, at least in the context of factual science, that *x* brings about, produces, or contributes to the production of *y*, and the mechanism of such production may be anything from almost pure chance to teleology, according to the nature of the case.

The further equality, *Lawfulness* = *Determinism*, is no less mistaken despite its popularity. Consider the central hypothesis of the steady-state cosmological theory, according to which matter is self-created *ex nihilo* at a pace slow enough to escape direct detection. This is a hypothesis of nonconservation, which is perfectly respectable as far as the principle of lawfulness is concerned—a principle that may be formulated thus: "Nothing occurs in a lawless, arbitrary, way." But the hypothesis of creation out of the blue conflicts with the genetic principle, according to which "Nothing arises out of nothing or goes into nothing," which can be regarded as an ontological generalization of all the conservation principles. The creation of matter is supposed to be not only *uncaused*—which would be unobjectionable—but also *indetermined,* that is, determined by nothing. Hence, the rate of creation could never be slowed down or accelerated by man, because no mechanism is provided upon which we might conceivably act: matter is said to just pop up magically here and there without any antecedent condition. This hypothesis, then, is *indeterministic* because, although it obeys the principle of lawfulness, it violates the genetic principle.[11]

Conversely, some theory might be advanced which postulated the occurrence of entirely lawless events which, still, would

[11] M. Bunge, "Cosmology and Magic," *The Monist,* 44, No. 1 (1962).

somehow be produced—even though erratically—by something else. If we were to accept some of the various popular misconceptions about the quantum theory, we would say that this theory violates the principle of lawfulness, merely because—at least in the orthodox version of the theory—it does not account for the details of the whereabouts of the individual microsystems, even though it does account for their collective behavior and for the behavior of collections of observations on individual systems.

We see, then, that the genetic principle and the postulate of lawfulness are logically independent of one another and that both are necessary and sufficient to build up a theory of *general determinism* making room for a wide class of categories of determination and kinds of law.[12]

According to this liberal version of determinism—which may be called neodeterminism—noncausal laws do not commit us to indeterminism but, rather, to a renewal of classical determinism. Only law-breakers and creationists (whether in magic, religion, or cosmology) would be indeterministic in this general sense of 'determinism.'

Since scientific research is essentially the search for law and the tracing of the lawful transformation or genesis of things and events out of other things and events, those interested in either law-breaking or creation *ex nihilo* should turn to politics, magic, parapsychology, contemporary British cosmology, or religion. Science is now as deterministic—*lato sensu*—as it ever was. But the philosophy of determinism must be modernized to keep pace with science, and the philosophical vocabulary of scientists should be brushed up.

[12] An exposition of general determinism, or neodeterminism, is found in *op. cit.* fn. 1. For a criticism of the opinion that quantum mechanics consecrates indeterminism, see my *Metascientific Queries* (Springfield, Ill.: Charles C. Thomas, Publisher, 1959), Chapters 8-10.

# 12

# Laws of Laws

One of the most exciting novelties in recent physics is the discovery that not every physical law is invariant under space inversion, i.e., that the law of conservation of parity does not hold universally.[1] In spite of the impact this discovery has had upon physical research and even upon our general outlook (since it involves the distinguishability of right and left in certain cases), there is room to doubt whether the "violation of parity" is always clearly understood—which should not be surprising, since the phrase refers ambiguously to two definitely separate categories of object: to law statements, and to facts. In fact, it

[1] T. D. Lee and C. N. Yang, *Physical Review,* 104 (1956), 254; C. S. Wu, E. Ambler, R. Hayward, D. D. Hoppes, and R. P. Hudson, *Physical Review,* 105 (1957), 1413.

may be taken as saying either that certain law statements do not remain invariant upon an exchange of left and right, or that certain processes lack mirror symmetry.

An analysis of the concept of statement about law statements, as distinct from statements about facts, should therefore prove helpful in clarifying not only the logical status but also the physical meaning of propositions concerning symmetry. The following, although illustrated mainly with statements about physical statements, transcends the scope of the philosophy of physics: the concept of law of law is as important in the entire field of factual science as is the corresponding notion of metatheorem in formal science.

## 1. *Metalaw Statements and Metanomological Statements*

Scientific texts contain both object statements (e.g., "$2 + 3 = 5$," "Water expands upon freezing") and metastatements (e.g., "The equality '$2 + 3 = 5$' is a theorem in ordinary arithmetics," "The law 'Water expands when freezing' is well known to plumbers").[2] While object statements refer to the objects (whether physical or not) dealt with in the corresponding piece of language, metastatements say something about further statements: they are not signs of primary objects but signs of signs; metastatements belong consequently in the metalanguage. So far, this is nursery semantics. But the failure to distinguish metastatements from object statements can be found at any age; and this failure is responsible for some of the muddles connected with the key concept of law of nature.

An important subclass of metastatements is constituted by those dealing with law statements, or scientific laws. Statements about law statements may be called *metalaw* statements. They may talk about any of the problems that cluster around the conjecturing, processing, testing, or application of regularities of any sort. Thus, metalaw statements may refer to the logical

[2] R. Carnap, *The Logical Syntax of Language* (London: Routledge and Kegan Paul, 1937; Paterson, N. J.: Littlefield, Adams & Co., 1959), Part V.

form of law statements (e.g., "Statistical laws are not general conditionals"), to their range of validity (e.g., "The law of the equivalence of mass and energy does not apply to fields"), to the adequate method of testing law statements (e.g., "The laws of physiology are tested by physico-chemical methods"), to their symmetry properties (e.g., "Maxwell's equations are invariant under space inversion"), and so forth. Some metalaw statements occur in ordinary language, others belong to science, and a few are the property of metascience. In no case are they laws of nature or laws of culture; they just refer to *statements* expressing in turn what are supposed to be objective laws of nature or culture.

Occasionally the distinction between law statements and metalaw statements seems vanishingly small. Thus, apparently, "Newton's law of gravitation holds for planetary systems" (a metalaw) is identical with "In all planetary systems, the bodies attract each other with a force proportional to the product of the masses and inversely proportional to the square of the distance between" (a law). The differences are these: (*a*) the referent of the metalaw statement is a law *statement,* namely, Newton's law of gravitation, whereas the referent of the law statement is a *thing,* or rather a class of things (namely, planetary systems); (*b*) the metalaw statement in question contains a pragmatic term, 'holds,' which is absent from the law statement; it is one thing to state a hypothesis, quite another to state that the hypothesis is true.

Attention will be focused in the following on a particularly interesting and neglected kind of metalaw statement: namely, the class of *lawlike* (or nomomorphous) statements about scientific laws—that is, the set of assertions that are general in some respect and to some extent, and which refer to scientific laws. More exactly, we will be concerned with a proper subclass of lawlike statements about law statements, namely, those which are well justified or, at any rate, accepted. "The law of conservation of parity does not hold for weak interactions," and

"The laws of heredity are rooted to the laws of chemistry," are members of this set of *lawful* metalaw statements.

Lawful metalaw statements differ from casual metalaw statements in that the former do not specify particular situations involving the use of law statements (as, e.g., in "Electricians employ Kirchhoff's laws") but *describe or prescribe basic traits of law statements.* The name *metanomological statement* can be given to this subclass of metalaw statements;[3] it is less ambiguous than the name law of law, because scientific laws, too, can be regarded as laws of laws if, in its second occurrence, the term 'law' is taken to denote objective pattern or nomic structure. The name metanomological statement is also more correct than the name law of law because—as will be seen in what follows —not all statements about laws are laws themselves; not all of them are capable of being true (since some of them are norms or prescriptions), although they are all more or less general and justified. But, of course, it is only through a linguistic convention that we assign different designata to 'metalaw statement' (the class of statements about law statements) and 'metanomological statement' (the proper subclass of lawful metalaw statements).

Before proceeding to survey the kinds of metanomological statement it will be convenient to examine a specimen. A good specimen is the following: "The region of validity of the simplifying approximations, of which any theory must necessarily make use, is always far wider than might be justified by theoretical arguments."[4] This metascientific statement does not refer to nature but to a universal trait of quantitative scientific *theories* (systems of propositions among which law statements are prominent); specifically, it refers to the performance of the auxiliary simplifying assumptions that are made in *every* at-

[3] M. Bunge, *Metascientific Queries (*Springfield, Ill.: Charles C. Thomas, Publisher, 1959), Chapter 4.

[4] N. Arley, *On the Theory of Stochastic Processes and Their Application to the Theory of Cosmic Radiation* (New York: John Wiley & Sons, 1943), p. 15.

tempt either to describe a state of affairs with the help of theoretical law statements or to explain it by building a theoretical model simple enough to be worked out. The quoted sentence covers, moreover, the performance of the simplifying assumptions involved in *any* quantitative nomological statement worthy of the name. Like any scientific law, the statement concerned transcends the set of available singular experiences (relating to such performances) and takes the risk of asserting that something—to wit, the region of validity of simplifying approximations—is *always* wider than might be expected before the test of experience. It is, then, a doubly universal metanomological statement. Of course, not all the metanomological statements have such a wide scope; they are all, however, general in some respect and to some extent, and they are all justified to some extent, even if only by practice.

Now, not all metanomological statements are alike; some are lawful statements about the status of scientific laws and others are criteria or, if preferred, requirements often imposed upon laws. In fact, at least three species of metanomological statements can be distinguished, which will be baptized *factual, normative,* and *methodological* metanomological statements. "Newton's laws of motion are invariant under time reversal" exemplifies factual metanomological statements. "The equations of motion are not to depend on any frame of reference" is an instance of normative metanomological statements. And "Law statements should not include egocentric particulars such as 'here' and 'now' " illustrates methodological metanomological statements. Let us examine them separately.

## 2. *Factual Metanomological Statements*

These are statements about *properties, performance* (domain of validity), or *usefulness* of nomological statements. They may be particular or universal, according as they refer to a few laws or to all the laws characterizing a given level or sublevel of reality. But factual metanomological statements are all general in the sense that they do not refer to particular instances of application of scientific laws. The proposition "The laws of thermodynamics are valid for all macroscopic systems" is an instance of particular metanomological statements; it is particular because it refers to a specific set of laws, but it is universal as regards the class of facts for which these laws are said to be valid—this range is open. On the other hand, a statement like the one referring to the domain of applicability of the approximations made in the law statements and in their consequents (see the previous section) is universal both as regards the range of the law statements and their variety. Another metanomological statement of universal scope is: "All the differential equations of science are derivable from variational principles." And "The laws of history are all statistical" is a universal metanomological statement in so far as it refers to all the laws of a certain field.

It should be kept in mind that factual metanomological statements *are not laws of nature or society* but assertions about law statements. "The equations of motion are invariant under canonical transformations" illustrates this point with particular clarity. In the first place, it is an analytic proposition if it is taken as an implicit definition of the phrase 'canonical transformations' (see Chapter 2). In the second place, canonical transformations (i.e., law-invariant changes of coordinates and momenta) are not, and do not reflect, processes taking place in nature, but are just changes in our *description* or *representation* of certain physical phenomena, on a par with changes in observation direction.[5] The fact that one and the same set of phenomena that "obey" a given set of equations of motion can be represented in an infinity of equivalent ways, is not a feature of physical systems but a trait of one of our descriptions of them. (Recall that the solutions to the basic equations of physics, not the equations of motion themselves, can be employed in the description of phenomena.) Hence the metanomological statement above is nothing but a (demonstrable) assertion about the

[5] See M. Bunge, *op. cit.* (fn. 4, Chapter 7).

language we employ in describing a certain level of nature; it says, in fact, that the relation phenomena-constructs is not one-one but one-infinity.

A similar problem is posed by time inversion; it is only psychologically more refractory owing to the difficulties of the time concept. This much-discussed question is considerably clarified if the transformation $t \rightarrow -t$ in the equations of motion is not regarded as something happening in the external world, but as a nonsignificant sign-exchange similar to canonical transformations (and actually equivalent to an anticanonical transformation). Even the Wigner time reversal (time inversion accompanied by complex conjugation) is of such a formal nature, although, for some mysterious reason, it is sometimes called physical time reversal in contrast with the former, formal time reversal. In fact, the Wigner time reversal enables us to obtain the reversed motions of particles and waves; and these backward motions take particles and waves as little to the past as does the projection of a motion picture in reversed order. 'Time reversal,' in the context of the theory of elementary particles, does not mean the exchange of past and future but the inversion of velocities and currents—and this, too, may be due to a mere change in "point of view" or representation.

The invariance of some basic physical variables and relations (e.g., laws) under time reversal is not a property of physical reality but a trait of some of the constructs that have been invented for the description and explanation of physical phenomena. Thus when we say that invariance under the (Wigner) time reversal is "violated" in certain elementary particle processes, we mean that the interaction Hamiltonian (energy operator) entering in the corresponding theory is not invariant under that *conceptual* operation. In the context of Newtonian mechanics we may choose to describe mechanical phenomena either by employing increasing times or by using decreasing times, as long as the forces are not of odd degree in their velocities; this has to do with *our* manner of reckoning time, not with the objective flux of phenomena. Similarly, we may decide to count time backwards and not forward in the context of electrodynamics; in this case all we have to do is to reverse the usual signs of fields and currents. It may seem an awkward procedure, but it is as legitimate as the usual one.

Electron theory in both its classical and quantal forms affords another illustration of the nature of time inversion—or, better, of the change in the sign of the *t*-variable. Positrons may be described *as if* they were electrons going backward in time.[6] But this possibility, ensured by the versatility of the basic equations, is a conceptual, not a material one; it does not entail the physical possibility of electrons paying a visit to the past. If it did, we would have the means for building a time machine and for changing the past, which would produce changes in the present, which in turn would give us new possibilities for repairing the past, and so on *ad infinitum*. We cannot go up the stream of events, we cannot undo what has happened; all we can do is to build clocks running contrariwise and to frame theories that are invariant under time inversion (or under the combined reversal of time and charge). If time were nothing but what we read on ideal frictionless clocks, there would be no objective "arrow" of time in each reference system.

The combined time and charge symmetry of the equations of motion does not mean that the positron *is* nothing but an electron with its proper time reversed; it means that, just as the equations of mechanics and of the electromagnetic field theory allow for an infinity of equivalent descriptions of phenomena, so the equations of motion of charged particles can be employed to describe certain qualitatively different processes without making any changes in the equations. One of the possible descriptions of the positron happens to be the time-and-charge mirror image of our usual description of the electron; this, far from pointing to a symmetry in nature, shows that our equations are ambivalent. And it cautions us not to

[6] R. P. Feynman, *Physical Review,* 76 (1949), 749.

mistake properties of signs for properties of their referents.[7]

As can be seen, the mere awareness of the existence of metanomological statements constitutes an effective reminder that not every general scientific statement refers to facts. Let us now apply the distinctions elaborated so far to the problem of space inversion.

### 3. *An Application: Nonconservation of Parity*

In 1956 a surprising metanomological statement was suggested—that the law of conservation of parity might not hold for certain physical processes, such as the beta-decay of atomic nuclei and muons. Now, when hearing that parity is not conserved in the interactions that are assumed to lead to these processes, we should distinguish three different meanings, connected respectively with: (1) the metatheory, (2) the top-statements of the theory, and (3) its bottom-statements. On the metatheoretical level, the statement in question can be framed thus: "The (tacit) hypothesis that the law of conservation of parity (or invariance under space inversion) is universally valid must be abandoned." Relative to the highest level of theory (the one in which the axioms occur), 'parity nonconservation' means that the field Hamiltonian occurring in the basic equations by means of which those processes are explained is not invariant under space reflections. In this case, too, a *metastatement* is clearly at stake, and no experiment is needed to test it, since it refers to a *mathematical* property of the Hamiltonian; experiments are required to decide among alternative Hamiltonians with different symmetry properties.

If from the highest level statements in the theory we come down to their empirically testable consequences, we find among others the formula for the angular distribution of the particles

[7] For a metascientific analysis of the theory of positrons and the meaning of Feynman's graphs, see M. Bunge, *Metascientific Queries,* Chapter 10.

emitted in beta-decay.[8] This low-level formula is descriptive of phenomena: it is an object statement. If it turns out that this formula is not parity-invariant (e.g., because it contains a pseudoscalar quantity), we shall have to distinguish: (*a*) statements about the *mathematical* symmetry properties of the formula concerned (which will be noninvariant under space reflection if the mother law is itself noninvariant); (*b*) statements about the *physical meaning* of the daughter formulas. It is the latter statements which, when checked against experimental data, show a marked asymmetry in the angular distribution of the emitted electrons. On the other hand, the statements about the mathematical properties of the low-level formulas are metalaw statements the truth value of which can be established by pencil and paper operations.

The actual process of checking metastatements concerning the invariance properties of the basic laws is, then, the following: (1) a Hamiltonian is set up which contains both *P*-invariant and *P*-noninvariant terms in unknown proportions: (2) experimentally testable consequences are mathematically derived from the law statement containing the trial Hamiltonian; (3) experiments are designed to test some new typical consequences of the basic hypothesis, and some outstanding experimentalist is captured for the project; (4) the corresponding observations and measurements (of, e.g., the angular distribution of the electrons emitted by aligned $Co^{60}$ nuclei) are planned and performed; (5) the experimental results are compared with the theoretical predictions; (6) the parameters (couplings) occurring in the basic law (and specifically in the Hamiltonian contained in the wave equation), and found again in the low-level formula for

[8] The formula is $I(\vartheta) = I_0\ (1 + A \cdot J \cdot p \cdot \cos\vartheta)$, where $A$, the asymmetry parameter, is experimentally found to be near $-1$. See, e.g., J. Hamilton, *The Theory of Elementary Particles* (Oxford: Clarendon Press, 1959), pp. 147-158; J. Serpe, *Les lois de conservation en physique des particules élémentaires* (Bruxelles: Institut Interuniversitaire des Sciences Nucléaires, 1959), pp. 31-34.

the angular distribution or any other empirically testable consequence, are adjusted to the experimental findings.

The process of validating the *metanomological* statements about the symmetry properties of basic laws is, then, purely analytic; only the process of validating the *basic laws* themselves, which are object statements, requires empirical procedures. The former are not descriptive of actual fact; facts are relevant only to the test of the *referents* of metanomological statements, i.e., the object law statements. Metanomological statements about symmetry properties of scientific laws are just assertions about properties of symbols; they have no direct empirical counterpart and they may contain terms which have no operational meaning. Thus the property called intrinsic parity (of state functions) has neither a classical analogue nor an empirical meaning, whence it cannot be regarded as a physical property on a par with mass or decay time. Intrinsic parity is, in fact, a mathematical property of wave functions and not a physical property of material systems, just as hermiticity is a formal property of operators. The intrinsic parity of states of physical systems cannot be measured apart from the theory describing them; a definite wave equation must first be assumed.

If familiar analogues of conservation and nonconservation of that typically quantum mechanical operator called parity are needed for didactic purposes, considerations other than the familiar ones referring to symmetries in things or in phenomena should be sought, because what the weak interactions "violate" is an *hypothesis* concerning a property of noniconic physical symbols acting as source-functions out of which representational symbols (such as the intensity of particle emission) can be derived. The following is offered as an analogue of parity "violation."

Let '*R*' stand for the property of a physical variable being real in the mathematical sense. With respect to many processes *R* is conserved, i.e., if the variable was initially real it remains real for all time; some processes, however, involve "violation of parity." Examples of such *R*-nonconservation processes are: (*a*) if a solenoid is added to an ohmic resistance in an electric circuit, the total resistance becomes a complex parameter; (*b*) in the passage of *X*-rays from glass to iron the refractive index of the medium changes into a complex number; (*c*) in the scattering of atomic projectiles by atomic nuclei a point is reached when the scattering potential, which is real in a certain energy range, becomes complex. In all these cases, to say that *R* is violated means that the *description* of certain processes requires the replacement of a real by a complex variable, because a new phenomenon occurs (electromagnetic induction in the first case, and absorption in the last two) for the description of which a new real variable is needed. The physical meaning of the phrase '*R* is violated' must then be sought in the *object* statements describing these new phenomena which are not accounted for by the hypothesis of *R*-invariance.

The case of *P*-invariance is similar, but somewhat more involved than its *R*-invariance analogue. In fact, two concepts of parity are involved in the ambiguous phrase "Parity is not conserved for weak interactions": (*a*) that of an analytic property of state functions, which are constructs referring to reality in an extremely indirect way, and (*b*) that of a property of certain physical processes (e.g., beta decay). In the first case the statement under consideration refers to the *laws* that are supposed to describe the phenomenon. It is therefore a metastatement and, specifically, a metanomological statement since, far from being concerned with a particular instance, it describes a basic trait of the laws involved in the theoretical account of weak interactions. In the second case the statement about parity nonconservation refers to certain phenomena accounted for by the law statement concerned, and is therefore an *object* statement.

Various morals can be drawn from the "parity violation" story. First, parity violation is a misnomer, since nothing is violated—only the refutation of a hypothesis is at stake. Secondly, a lot of confusion can be saved if ambiguity is reduced by stating carefully *what* is to be regarded as symmetrical (or invariant) in a certain sense, i.e., under certain transformations

—things (e.g., bodies), phenomena (e.g., particle emission), properties of systems or phenomena (e.g., angular distribution), theoretical terms more or less closely related with properties (e.g., interaction Hamiltonians), basic law statements (e.g., equations of motion) or, finally, derivative law statements that can be tested by experiment (e.g., formulas in which both the direction of motion and the sense of spin "rotation" occur). Such an explicit indication would suffice to determine whether, when symmetries (or invariances) are discussed, object statements or metastatements are meant. Thirdly, although we control our pictures of reality by means of experiment and observation, the statements about statements occurring in those pictures are not themselves descriptive of fact; in particular, metanomological statements—whether factual or not—are definitely not directly descriptive. Fourthly, the most (perhaps the only) dangerous assumptions in science are those which are made unwittingly—as was the case with the metanomological statement "All physical laws are invariant under space inversion." This tacit sweeping assumption—an induction from a few cases—has facilitated work; but, on the other hand, it has prevented for thirty years various theoretical developments, such as trying *P*-noninvariant interaction Hamiltonians, and working out the two-component neutrino theory, which had been sketched and abandoned in 1929 for not being parity-invariant. Fifthly, the obvious is sometimes (perhaps usually) wrong, and the most reliable nomological and metanomological statements may fail in some domain; they all remain hypotheses even after repeated favorable tests, so that a dogmatic attitude towards any of them is incompatible with a scientific spirit.

## 4. *The Truth Value of Factual Metanomological Statements: The Analytic Variety*

Granting that there are metanomological statements, the question now arises whether and how they can be true. After establishing that a statement *can* be true (a syntactical and semantical problem) we may inquire *how* it is tested (a methodological affair) and, finally, *whether* it is in fact true to a good approximation (a scientific problem).

That factual metanomological statements, which are of the form 'The laws $L$ have the property $P$,' can be true seems clear. We can always ascertain, at least in principle, whether a given set of statements, be they nomological or not, does have the property ascribed to it by another statement, provided the object statement and the metastatement are both well formed and do not contain exceedingly vague words, such as 'simple.'

Consider that distinguished newcomer, the Lüders-Pauli combined parity theorem, which can be formulated thus: "If a local field theory is Lorentz invariant, then it is also invariant under the combined inversion of charge ($C$), time ($T$), and parity ($P$)." (Actually, '$T$' stands for $t$-reversal combined with conjugation or even a more involved operation.) Let us first make sure whether this statement expresses a law of nature—as seems to be usually believed. Clearly, the $CTP$ theorem deals with certain *conceptual* operations (reversing the signs of the charge and of the space-time coordinates) that may be performed on the formulas expressing the laws of nature that the basic equations of field theories are (charitably) supposed to reproduce on the conceptual level. Nucleons, electrons, and other entities which we attempt to describe by means of field theories are not observed to rush into the past, or to reverse their directions of motion, or to transmute spontaneously into their antiparticles, just because we decide to reckon formerly positive time, position coordinates, and charge values as negative. Only a change in the mode of description is involved in the $CTP$ reversal operations.

It is clear that the sign reversals involved in the $CTP$ theorem do not refer to the phenomena accounted for by the field theories but to their *description* with the help of such constructs; the theorem states that the description of elementary particle processes can be made in two equivalent ways, one of which is the mirror image of the other. In fact, the theorem says nothing about symmetries found in phenomena, which are described by means of the *solutions* to the basic equations. The *CTP* theorem is a statement about certain symmetries (or invariances) found in *basic law statements;* those symmetries recur in some of the low-level consequents of the basic equations. The *CTP* theorem is, then, a typically metanomological statement, even though a careless glance may show it as an object statement and, specifically, as a law of nature. What is true is that a further, more readily understandable metalaw statement can be inferred from the *CTP* theorem in conjunction with the additional hypothesis of separate *T*-invariance and the definition of 'antimatter' (composed of positive electrons, antiprotons, etc.); namely, "Antimatter obeys the same basic laws as matter does." That this, too, is a metastatement is clear: it amounts to the assertion that "antimatter" (what an unfortunate name!) does not call for the invention of new theories (for the time being), as the available relativistic theories are bivalent: they hold (very roughly indeed) for both the familiar world and its possible dual. (Notice, incidentally, the analogy of this metalaw statement with duality principles in mathematics, e.g., in projective geometry, where the metastatement is found "If the terms 'point' and 'plane' are exchanged in a theorem, a new, true proposition is obtained"; they, too, are metastatements and enable the saving of work.)

Why is the *CTP* theorem said to work? Experimenters have not put it to the test. How could they? What they have subjected to experiment is the *object* statements referred to by the *CTP* theorem. How could they test the *CTP* theorem in the laboratory if it does not speak primarily about phenomena but about modes of description? To undertake the empirical test of the combined parity theorem would be like trying to prove by experiment that any given set of equations of motion can be derived from an infinity of Lagrangians differing from one another only by the divergence of an arbitrary vector. Whatever truth there is in the *CTP* theorem, it derives from purely mathematical procedures. It is an *analytic* proposition (in the sense elucidated in Chapter 2). This does not mean that it is a physically arbitrary statement; after all, it does refer to object statements that are empirically tested. Hence, the theorem will stand or fall together with the rest of the theory, i.e., ultimately by virtue of empirical evidence, even though it is not checked by experiment.

As a second example of analytic metanomological statements consider the heuristic principle "All physical law statements are derivable from variational principles"—which is a ground for the exhortation to discover upper level statements of great unifying power in all branches of physical science. This statement is true in relation to that important subclass of physical law statements that can be given the form of differential equations (since every variational equation implies one or more differential equations). But it is a fact that integral and integro-differential equations cannot be so derived, and yet we need them to account for hereditary phenomena. Hence, as it stands, the above metanomological statement is not altogether adequate; it should be rephrased to read, instead, "All statements expressible as differential equations are derivable from variational principles." And in this form its syntactical or formal nature is apparent: it is a mathematical truth, hence an analytic proposition. It may function as a guiding rule in research, but its truth is independent of any physical assumption.

We conclude that some factual metanomological statements are justified by purely logical or mathematical operations; consequently we should drop the qualifier 'factual' in connection with them and call them instead *analytic metanomological statements.* Since they are analytic propositions, experience cannot refute them; but it can render them pointless.

## 5. *The Synthetic Variety of Factual Metanomological Statements*

Other metanomological statements do not fit so closely in scientific or mathematical theories as the analytic metanomological statements do; they cannot be *demonstrated,* although they can be validated or justified a posteriori. This is the case with those metanomological statements that function as superpostulates of a theory.

Consider the principle of general covariance, a postulate or, rather, superpostulate, of general relativity. It can be phrased in dozens of more or less equipollent ways: sometimes as an object statement, occasionally as a metastatement, and often in an ambiguous way. An instance of the former kind of formulation is "All systems of coordinates mutually transformable by arbitrary point-transformations are physically equivalent." On the other hand, "The equations expressing basic physical laws are form-invariant with respect to general continuous coordinate transformations," is clearly a metanomological statement. Still other formulations can be interpreted in either way, because they contain the ambiguous phrase 'laws of nature,' which may designate either an objective pattern (in which case an object statement is at stake) or a nomological statement (in which case we have to do with a metanomological statement). Instances of such ambiguity are "The laws of nature do not depend on any privileged reference system," "The laws of nature hold for systems of reference in any kind of motion," and "The laws of nature do not depend on the observer's frame of reference."

The justification for asserting metanomological statements of this kind lies in the fruit they bear, i.e., in the success of the *object* statements they refer to. In turn this success is measured, of course, by the object statement's yield (in conjunction with further law statements and with bits of empirical information) of true predictions and far-reaching explanations. Being an axiom of a factual theory, the principle of general covariance in its metanomological guise may well be corrected or even abandoned (although at the present time a radical change in it looks unlikely because of its deep philosophical bearing, to the extent to which it says, among other things, that the object-laws of physics are independent of the operator, whence the attempts to interpret the relativity theory in operationalistic terms are doomed to failure).

Something similar can be said in connection with another basic metanomological statement, namely, "Correct field theories are gauge-invariant," which can also be formulated in a deontic way, namely thus: "Field theories must be gauge-invariant." Notice first that *theories*—and in particular their basic statements, the fundamental field equations or the variational principles that yield them—are hereby required to be invariant under certain transformations; not the fields but the field *equations* are to be invariant under certain changes in the field variables (potentials or wave functions). Notice further that infinite alternative descriptions of every set of facts are thereby declared to be equivalent to one another. (This is congruous with the interpretation according to which the functions undergoing the gauge transformations—e.g., the electromagnetic potentials—have no independent physical meaning in the context of the free field theory, but are source-functions out of which physically meaningful functions, such as the field strengths, can be derived. Potentials acquire a physical meaning in Hamiltonian theories of charged particles, where they are seen to contribute to the particle momentum; they are also physically effective according to quantum mechanics, since they may produce phase differences and consequently interference effects.)[9]

It seems then clear that the principle of gauge invariance is a metanomological statement. Of course, it is not an arbitrary dictum; we accept it because its "violation" would have false consequences, at least in ordinary electrodynamics. In fact, the non-conservation of the electromagnetic field equations with respect to gauge transformations would entail: (*a*) the nonconservation of the electric charge, in contradiction with the best empirical evidence, and (*b*) the existence of a photon mass, which contradicts both empirical evidence and the special theory of relativity (notwithstanding the many textbooks which assign

[9] For the significance of electromagnetic potentials in the quantum theory, see Y. Aharonov and D. Bohm, *Physical Review,* 115 (1959), 485; 123 (1961), 1511.

a mass to the photon by virtue of the theorem of mass and energy equivalence, a theorem which is deduced in the relativistic mechanics of particles, not in field theory.) The metanomological statement regarding gauge invariance will, of course, be dispensed with in electrodynamic theories without potentials[10] —which shows once again that the principle of gauge invariance is not a law of nature but a restriction imposed upon certain law statements in order to preclude false consequences.

In short, factual metanomological statements are hypotheses to be validated, in the last instance, by experiment and by their agreement with the accepted metascientific (e.g., epistemological) principles; they are not simply syntactical sentences of the same type as "The term 'law' is a universal word." Nor are they directly testable in the laboratory; factual metanomological statements, if not analytic, are hypotheses supported or rebutted by the performance of the object law statements to which they refer.

## 6. *Normative Metanomological Statements*

These are *extralogical and extraepistemological conditions* imposed upon law statements, and they function as rules restricting their possible choice. The best known representative of this kind of higher order statement is probably the principle of special relativity, namely, "The laws of motion must be the same in all reference frames moving in uniform translation relatively to each other." (Incidentally, this shows once again that physical theories, far from being all one-floor buildings, may be duplex constructions in which both object statements and metastatements occur.)

Normative metanomological statements are not requirements of a philosophical sort, like the logical (and controvertible) condition that all law statements must be general conditionals of the form 'For all $x$, if $x$ is $P$, then $x$ is $Q$,' or like the epistemolog-

[10] See L. Infeld and J. Plebanski, *Proceedings of the Royal Society,* A 222 (1954), 224.

ical (and equally controvertible) requisite that all law statements ought to contain directly observable predicates only. The framing and discussion of normative metanomological statements is usually made by scientists, not by philosophers; moreover, certain regulative principles of this kind are often the main torchlights physicists employ in theory construction, particularly on the frontier line.

It will be noticed that it is always possible to frame normative metanomological statements so as to confer upon them the appearance of referring, not to statements which are in turn about objective patterns, but solely to our handling of certain symbols called law statements. That is, they may be interpreted as being nothing but rules for the formation of some language game which is not, in turn, about anything going on in the external world. Thus the principle of general relativity may be read as simply a requirement about the literal invariance (form invariance) of the basic equations, or about their geometrical properties (as, e.g., in "The form of the basic equations must not change under arbitrary point-transformations"). Such formulations undoubtedly shed light on the syntactical properties of the general covariance principle; but they are irrelevant to its content, which is the assertion of the objectivity of the laws of nature and, as a consequence, of their invariance under possible changes, on *our* part, in point of view or mode of description (or choice of reference system). In this sense, the following formulations are preferable because they are richer: "The equations of motion must not depend on the choice of the reference system," and "No system of reference is to be singled out in preference to any other, except for convenience of computation." (Whether these statements are adequate is another story.)

It is also possible to frame all normative metanomological statements as if they referred only to modes of observation and, moreover, to observation in itself, not to the observation *of* some physical system or event—which possibility does not involve the adequacy of such a translation. Thus certain quantum-mechanical postulates can be given an operational flavor by replacing in them 'dynamical variable' by 'observable'—although the quantum-mechanical operators called observables are related to observational data in a very indirect fashion. In this way it is possible to force those statements into the Procrustean bed of the philosophical prescription according to which "Physical theories should consist only of relations among observable quantities, and should have as their sole aim the prediction of empirically obtainable quantities." [11] But such a reformulation of nomological and metanomological statements in terms of observations and of observation predicates is a verbal manoeuvre and obscures the actual situation, since it gives those statements the appearance of referring *solely* to human experience, and not to nature as well. Moreover, they perform a persuasive rather than a clarifying function, since their aim is to persuade us that the variables of theoretical physics are not elaborate constructs the (rational) values of which are assigned through long and twisted theoretico-empirical procedures (deduction and measurement), but are observational terms like color and taste names, nicely complying with the requirements of a narrow sort of empiricism.[12]

True, normative metanomological statements are not laws of nature but prescriptions regarding laws of nature, and can consequently be used as heuristic clues for the invention of further

[11] That this was a heuristic rule and not a physical principle, was explicitly recognized by M. Born and P. Jordan, *Elementare Quantenmechanik* (Berlin: Springer, 1930), p. 14. Whether it actually served for building such high-level constructs as occur in matrix and wave mechanics is another, implausible story, disbelieved by the originator of operationalism himself. See P. W. Bridgman, *The Nature of Physical Theory* (New York: Dover Publications Inc., 1936), p. 65.

[12] The impossibility of framing operational definitions of physical quantities is realized when it is recalled that (*a*) no measurement can yield an irrational number, and (*b*) no measurement can replace the formation of a concept, however much it may clarify it. See C. G. Hempel: "The Concept of Cognitive Significance: A Reconsideration," *Proceedings of the American Academy of Arts and Sciences,* 80 (1951), 61, and A. Pap, "Are Physical Magnitudes Operationally Definable?," in C. W. Churchman and P. Ratoosh (Eds.), *Measurement: Definitions and Theories* (New York: John Wiley & Sons, 1959).

law statements. But this does not prevent them from referring, in a mediate way, to the referents of the law statements themselves, which are nature or culture (or simplified models of bits of nature or culture).

It should also be noticed that some statements, looking at first blush normative, are actually disguised definitions or, at least, tacit specifications of the meanings of certain terms. A case in point is the following sentence: "The exact laws of nature [meaning the fundamental laws of physics] must not contain any material constants; the latter should be derived from those laws on the basis of the atomic structure of the material under investigation." [13] This is not a normative metanomological statement but rather a partial specification of the meaning of the phrase 'exact law' (which in this context means fundamental physical law, or physical axiom regarding the "fundamental" components of matter). It is a metalaw but not a metanomological statement, and the modal particle 'must' that occurs in it is, to this extent, dispensable; it might as well be replaced by 'do.'

Finally, it is possible to argue that norms may all be translated, without loss of either meaning or practical effect, into declarative sentences.[14] Thus "Field theories *must* be gauge invariant" can be translated into "*Correct* field theories employing potentials *are* gauge invariant." But, quite apart from the possibility of translating modal and deontic sentences into declarative ones, it is a fact that, at least at the pragmatic level, some metanomological statements are prescriptive rather than descriptive.

## 7. *Methodological Metanomological Statements*

These are *logical or epistemological conditions* imposed upon law statements and, like the normative metanomological ones,

[13] H. Weyl, *Philosophy of Mathematics and Natural Science,* 2nd ed. (Princeton, N. J.: Princeton University Press, 1949), p. 162.

[14] M. Bunge, *Etica y ciencia* (Buenos Aires: Siglo Veinte, 1960); "Ethics as a Science," *Philosophy and Phenomenological Research,* 22 (1961), 139.

they serve as rules guiding our choice of law statements. Conspicuous members of this class of metascientific statements are the following: "Nomological statements ought not to contain egocentric particulars like 'I' or 'this,'" "Nomological statements ought not to be confidently accepted unless and until they become parts of conceptual nets (theories)," "Nomological statements may contain high level constructs (logical constructions like 'average' and theoretical terms like 'spin') on condition that they, or other law statements logically connected with them, establish bridges between those constructs and low-level concepts having empirical correlates."

Scientists make free use of methodological metanomological statements; but, of course, as soon as they state, discuss, and reject them overtly, they act *qua* metascientists, i.e., as philosophers. Statements of this kind are, moreover, favorite preys of logicians and metascientists, who have often proposed criteria of laws, though in most cases without paying close attention to the actual use of the word 'law' in the sciences. A consequence of this aprioristic attitude is that some of their criteria (e.g., the requisite of unrestricted universality, or the restriction to operationally definable concepts) are so unrealistic that investigators either do not pay attention to them or obey such ukases with no obvious benefit for science—as is the case of those historians and philosophers of science who deny the possibility of finding laws of history merely because no historical regularity could possibly be strictly universal and expressible in quantitative terms. (See Chapter 10.)

Metascientists wishing to set up logical and epistemological conditions of lawfulness—i.e., methodological metanomological statements—must struggle against the almost unavoidable tendency to draw on obsolete scientific information, e.g., on outdated data about the actual usages of the term 'law' in scientific quarters. Usage is certainly not the ultimate court of appeal, but it is the starting point of analysis if our elucidations are to be of any use whatsoever. Now, the present usage of the word 'law' in factual science is restricted neither to designating empirical regularities, as was the case before the birth of theoretical physics, nor to designating strictly universal theoretical statements; 'law' is nowadays the name for a host of statements of varying degrees of generality and precision. Criteria of lawfulness, expressed in methodological metanomological statements, should accordingly be regarded as changing, just as the normative metanomological statements are not beheld as unshakeable.

We conclude that scientists and metascientists utter metanomological statements of a prescriptive nature in relation to logical and epistemological characteristics of law statements; and that such norms, if realistic, must not be concocted as a priori regulative principles; they will have directive force to the extent to which they are fertile or, at least, nonobstructive—a necessary condition for sound metascience.

## 8. *The Status of Normative and Methodological Metanomological Statements*

We have seen that factual metanomological statements can be true or false. What about the remaining species of metanomological statements, exemplified by "Physical laws are to be independent of place and time?" Their form is not 'Laws *L* *have* the property *P*,' but 'Laws *L* *ought to have* the property *P*.' This shows that they are in the nature of rules (for theory construction), prescriptions, or norms; they are *proposals*, injunctions, or desiderata rather than propositions. Since they are, then, criteria, conditions, or requirements (like the correspondence principle, or the principle of scrutability), normative and methodological metanomological statements can be neither true nor false. Like all other proposals they can be relevant or irrelevant, expedient or obstructive, fertile or sterile and last, but not least, they can be consistent or inconsistent with a given philosophical standpoint.

Normative and methodological statements cannot be verified since they are not even capable of being false. However, they are not arbitrary commands or judgments of taste either. They are justified or vindicated,[15] in the first place, by *pragmatic* considerations, i.e. by appealing to desiderata previously agreed on, such as unifying power, or fertility. Metanomological statements of the normative and methodological kinds can also be justified *theoretically,* by showing their consistency with other statements of the same sort and with object law statements, as well as by showing the solidity of their presuppositions. Similarly, the command "Open the window," though not descriptive of actual fact and not even entitled to be false, may be *founded* or not. Thus, if the room is stuffy, the command is pragmatically justified by the desire of breathing fresh air, and is theoretically justified by hygiene.[16]

Now, that which cannot dispense with pragmatic justification —e.g., by the expediency of the course it recommends—is both logically and methodologically of the same kind as an exhortation like "Do not read: Watch *TV*." Normative and methodological statements are as little pieces of knowledge as are norms like "Science ought to benefit mankind as a whole," or invitations like "Let us build a philosophically sound demonstration of the second law of thermodynamics on the basis of statistical mechanics." Sure enough, the *referents* of normative and methodological metanomological statements are pieces of knowledge and, moreover, we may ignore such and such metanomological statements; but the fact that we can know them and ascertain the cognitive content of their referents does not require that they be pieces of knowledge. Normative and methodological metanomological statements afford a knowledge of *science* rather than a knowledge of nature or society, just as becoming acquainted with the ad "Do not read: Watch *TV*," affords no knowledge about either reading material or *TV* sets, but rather about advertising.

[15] For an elucidation of 'vindication' see H. Feigl, "Validation and Justification," in W. Sellars and J. Hospers (Eds.), *Readings in Ethical Theory* (New York: Appleton-Century-Crofts, 1952), pp. 667 ff.

[16] The possibility of affording theoretical justifications of norms is explored in the works cited in footnote 14.

Now, if truth or corroboration are required from law statements, neither normative nor methodological statements can be regarded as *laws* (see Chapter 10, section 5); they cannot even be regarded as *statements,* since the predicates 'true' and 'false' are pointless with regard to them. They are metanomological *proposals* rather than statements. This should not be surprising; metasentences need not have the same properties as their referents. Thus "I prefer variables to constants" belongs to psychology even though it refers to logical and mathematical objects. By the same token, a sentence like "Physical law statements ought to be independent of the observer's state of motion" is not a physical law even though it does belong to the multilevel language of physical science. The title of this chapter, then, is not altogether correct: it covers factual, but not normative or methodological metanomological statements.

Finally, the possible objection should be met that factual metanomological statements can all be construed as norms. Thus "Correct physical theories *are* relativistically invariant" can be translated into "Physical theories *ought to* be relativistically invariant." This is certainly true, and even trivially so if the correctness of theories is granted as a separate desideratum. But this translatability from the indicative into the normative form does not alter the logical status of factual metanomological statements, which—unlike the remaining species of metanomological sentences—have definite truth values.

## 9. *Summary and Conclusions*

To sum up, we may say that among the metastatements found in factual science a subclass of high heuristic value and philosophic interest is found: namely, the growing set of metanomological sentences, or lawful sentences about scientific laws. Some of them are generalizations—of various scopes—about law statements; others are norms, or rules of procedure, or criteria. The recognition of the metanomological character of various deep assertions occurring in contemporary physics—such as theorems about symmetry properties of certain physical laws—may be helpful in reducing the prevailing confusion in their regard, merely by showing that such statements do not refer directly to nature but to our modes of description. However, even though the disclosure of more or less covert metanomological statements in scientific discourse may be of some consequence for scientific research, it is more important for the understanding of science. In addition, the logical and epistemological analysis of metanomological sentences is interesting in itself—at least for the metascientist.

Furthermore, the mere existence of metanomological sentences shows that (*a*) not only facts, but the laws of facts as well, are usually assumed to be lawful; (*b*) factual science is not concerned with facts alone: it is also engaged in the establishment of statements about law statements; (*c*) science, like ethics, contains precepts, whence the language of science cannot be qualitatively distinct from the language of ethics, although ethical norms may outnumber scientific norms; (*d*) scientists face not only problems of validation but also problems of valuation and pragmatical and theoretical justification of norms, and such questions come up in every field of research, whether dealing with human behavior or not.

In short, the view is strengthened that, regarded as a body of knowledge (and not as an activity), science is more than a set of propositions: it is a set of systems of propositions and proposals of many kinds (data, laws, rules, criteria, etc.) arranged in various levels, and justified in various ways, though with a single aim: the maximization of the degree of truth. The increasing realization of this desirable and growing complexity of science should contribute to the withering away of the Cult of Simplicity.

# Index

## S



## T